# INTRODUCTION
# TO CROP HUSBANDRY

PERGAMON
INTERNATIONAL
LIBRARY
of Science, Technology
Engineering &
Social Studies

# INTRODUCTION TO CROP HUSBANDRY

THIRD EDITION

BY

J. A. R. LOCKHART, B.Agr.(Dist.)

AND

A. J. L. WISEMAN, N.D.A., C.D.A.

ROYAL AGRICULTURAL COLLEGE, CIRENCESTER

## PERGAMON PRESS

Oxford · New York · Toronto
Sydney · Braunschweig

Pergamon Press Ltd., Headington Hill Hall, Oxford

Pergamon Press Inc., Maxwell House, Fairview Park, Elmsford,
New York 10523

Pergamon of Canada Ltd., 207 Queen's Quay West, Toronto 1

Pergamon Press (Aust.) Pty. Ltd., 19a Boundary Street,
Rushcutters Bay, N.S.W. 2011, Australia

Pergamon Press GmbH, Burgplatz 1, Braunschweig 3300, West Germany

First edition 1966

Second edition 1970

Third edition 1975

*Printed in Great Britain by Biddles Ltd, Guildford, Surrey*

**Library of Congress Cataloging in Publication Data**

Lockhart, J. A. R.
Introduction to crop husbandry.

1. Field crops. I. Wiseman, A. J. L., joint author. II. Title.
SB185.L82 1975     633     74-10000
ISBN 0 08 018115 5
ISBN 0 08 018105 8 (pbk.)

# CONTENTS

## Chapter 3. *Fertilizers and Manures*

## Chapter 4. *Cropping*

## Chapter 5. *Grassland*

# FOREWORD

IN commending this book I would like to stress the importance of making the rudiments of agriculture available at Farm Institute and Day Release level. It is our technicians, our foremen and stockmen, as much as our farmers and farm managers, who will require intellectual assurance as well as intuitive skill if agriculture is to match in technological advance the manufacturing industries of the future. Agriculture has peculiar problems of its own which lie in the fields either of engineering, animal nutrition or agronomy. Mr. Lockhart and Mr. Wiseman have produced a book which deals comprehensively with the last category in a manner that should not be too advanced for the arable foreman of tomorrow. They give the subject a modern slant by incorporating such matters as the selective control of weeds, the principles of crop storage and field meteorology within the traditional framework of geology, botany and chemistry. In short they take much of the scientific mystery out of the subject by describing in basic terms those forces which promote and those factors which inhibit the growth of economic plants. This then is a grammar without which modern farming will not again become an art.

Whitehall Place, S.W.1.          JOHN GREEN
                                 Chairman of the
                                 Agricultural Advisory Council
                                 for England and Wales

# PREFACE

THIS book is an introduction to the science and practice of crop husbandry. It is written in simple language without losing its technical value. Young people doing their practical training will find it helpful for explaining modern farming practices of growing and harvesting crops. All aspects of the subject are dealt with, such as the growth and development of plants, types and management of soils, drainage and irrigation, modern practices of growing and harvesting crops, management of grassland—including conservation, typical life-cycles of common pests and diseases, and the latest developments in the use of chemicals as fertilizers and in the control of weeds, pests and diseases. Suggestions for classwork are also included at the end of sections.

Students taking the City and Guilds General Agriculture (Part 1) and similar examinations can use it as a textbook, and those taking higher examinations will find the book a valuable source of basic information which will be enlarged on in their courses.

The authors acknowledge with very grateful thanks the valuable help given by their wives in preparing and typing the manuscript.

J. A. R. LOCKHART
A. J. L. WISEMAN

Cirencester

# PREFACE TO
# THE SECOND EDITION

AGRICULTURE is no exception to the progress being made in the majority of industries in this country. This brings inevitable changes, and although it is less than four years since the first edition was published, many parts of this book have been completely revised. At the request of the publishers, the metric system has been adopted with the Imperial units (sometimes approximate) given only as alternatives. This, it is hoped, will meet the need for examination purposes in our Agricultural Colleges, although it is expected that it will be some years before metrication is fully in operation in the Agricultural industry. No official recommendations have yet been published as to all the units which are to be used in future, and for this edition guidance has had to be taken from those at present used on the Continent. A conversion table is included as an appendix.

As a result of the Recommendations of the Pilkington Report, courses at Agricultural Colleges are undergoing a transformation. This book is again intended for City and Guilds General Agricultural Students and for those concerned with the Ordinary National Diploma and similar courses. Higher National Diploma students will, it is hoped, find Introduction to Crop Husbandry a useful basis for this new Diploma, and students at Colleges of Estate Management should find that this book follows quite closely their Crop Husbandry Syllabus.

In preparing this second edition, particular acknowledgment is made to Mr. W. Heatherington for his valuable advice concerning the Pest section of the book.

J. A. R. LOCKHART
A. J. L. WISEMAN

Cirencester

# PREFACE TO
# THE THIRD EDITION

PARTS of the book have been revised and enlarged, with new techniques emphasized where considered necessary. Appropriate additions have also been included concerning regulations because of EEC membership.

After some deliberation it was decided to retain the Imperial Unit for this edition, although it will be realized that in 1975 the metric system will be the officially recognized unit of weight and measure in agriculture.

As before, grateful acknowledgement is made to our colleagues for helpful comment and this particularly applies to the chapter on Pests and Diseases of Farm Crops.

J. A. R. LOCKHART
A. J. L. WISEMAN

Cirencester

# INTRODUCTION

*Crops* are plants which have been carefully selected and developed to produce food for man and animals.

*Crop husbandry* is the practice of growing and harvesting crops. The main objective is to produce good crops as economically as possible without impoverishing the land.

The methods used have been developed over the past centuries from practical experience and experiments. In recent years there have been many sweeping changes as the result of:

(a) introduction of many new and improved varieties,
(b) better use of fertilizers,
(c) better control of pests and diseases,
(d) chemical weed control,
(e) rapid improvements in the mechanization of such operations as seed-bed preparation, planting, harvesting and storage.

An understanding of how plants grow, and what they need, is a useful guide when providing for their requirements.

Good crop husbandry is really good management of crop plants so that they are provided with the best possible conditions for growth.

# CHAPTER 1

# PLANTS

### What they Are; What they Do; and How they Live

Plants are living organisms consisting of innumerable tiny cells. They differ from animals in many ways but the most important difference is that plants can build up valuable organic substances from simple materials. The most important part of this building process, which is called *photosynthesis,* is the production of *carbohydrates* such as *sugars, starches* and *cellulose.*

PHOTOSYNTHESIS

In photosynthesis a special green substance called *chlorophyll* uses *light* energy (normally sunlight) to change *carbon dioxide* and *water* into *sugars* (carbohydrates) in the *green* parts of the plant. The daily amount of photosynthesis is limited by the duration and intensity of sunlight. The amount of carbon dioxide available is also a limiting factor. Shortage of water and low temperatures can also reduce photosynthesis.

The cells which contain chlorophyll also have yellow pigments such as *carotene.* Crop plants can only build up chlorophyll in the light and so any leaves which develop in the dark are yellow and cannot produce carbohydrates.

*Oxygen* is released during photosynthesis and the process may be set out as follows:

$$\text{Carbon dioxide} + \text{water} + \text{energy} \xrightarrow[\text{(light)}]{\text{chlorophyll}} \text{carbohydrates} + \text{oxygen}$$
$$nCO_2 \qquad nH_2O \qquad = \qquad (CH_2O)n \qquad nO_2$$

1

This process not only provides the basis for all our food but it also supplies the oxygen which animals and plants need for respiration.

The simple carbohydrates, such as *glucose*, may build up to form *starch* for storage purposes, or to *cellulose* for building cell walls. *Fats* and *oils* are formed from carbohydrates. *Protein* material, which is an essential part of all living cells, is made from carbohydrates and nitrogen compounds.

Most plants consist of *roots*, *stems*, *leaves* and *reproductive parts* and need *soil* in which to grow.

The *roots* spread through the spaces between the particles in the soil and anchor the plant. In a plant such as wheat the root system may total many miles.

The *leaves*, with their broad surfaces, are the main parts of the plant where photosynthesis occurs (see Fig. 1).

A very important feature of the leaf structure is the presence of large numbers of tiny pores (*stomata*) on the surface of the leaf (see Fig. 2). There are usually thousands of stomata per square inch of leaf surface. Each pore (stoma) is oval-shaped and surrounded by two guard cells. When the guard cells are turgid (full of water) the stoma is open and when they lose water the stoma closes.

The carbon dioxide used in photosynthesis *diffuses* into the leaf through the stomata and most of the water vapour leaving the plant, and the oxygen from photosynthesis diffuses out through the stomata.

TRANSPIRATION

The evaporation of water from plants is called *transpiration*. It mainly occurs through the stomata and has a cooling effect on the leaf cells. Water in the cells of the leaf can pass into the pore spaces in the leaf and then out through the stomata as water vapour (see Fig. 3).

The rate of transpiration varies considerably. It is greatest when the plant is well supplied with water and the air outside the leaf is warm and dry. In very hot or windy weather water evaporates from the guard cells and so the stomata close and reduce the rate of transpiration. The stomata also close in very cold weather e.g. 0°C (32°F).

The rate of loss is reduced if the plant is short of water because the guard cells then lose water and close the stomata; it is also retarded if the humidity of the atmosphere is high.

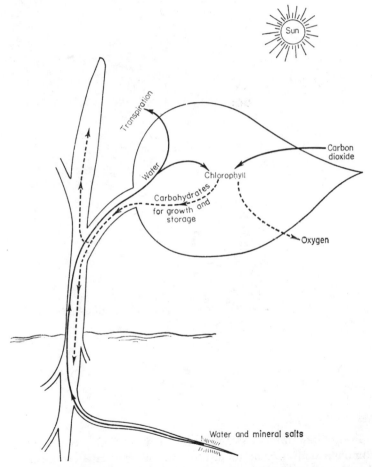

FIG. 1. Photosynthesis illustrated diagrammatically.

The stomata guard cells close (and so transpiration ceases) during darkness. They close because photosynthesis ceases and water is lost from the guard cells (osmosis) when some of the sugars present change to starch.

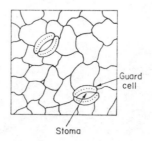

FIG. 2. Stomata on leaf surface.

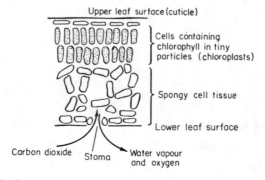

FIG. 3. Cross-section of a green leaf showing gaseous movements during daylight.

RESPIRATION

Plants, like animals, breathe, i.e. they take in oxygen which combines with organic foodstuffs and this releases energy, carbon dioxide and water. Farm crops are likely to be checked in growth if the roots are deprived of oxygen for respiration as might occur in a waterlogged soil.

TRANSLOCATION

The movement of materials through the plant is known as *translocation*.

The *xylem* or *wood vessels* which carry the water and mineral salts (*sap*) from the roots to the leaves are tubes made from dead cells. The cross walls of the cells have disappeared and the longitudinal walls are thickened with *lignum* to form wood. These tubes help to strengthen the stem.

The *phloem tubes* (*bast*) carry organic material through the plant, for example, sugars and amino acids from the leaves to storage parts or growing points. These vessels are chains of living cells, not lignified, and with cross walls which are perforated—hence the alternative name—*sieve tubes*.

In the stem the xylem and phloem tubes are usually found in a ring near the outside of the stem.

In the root, the xylem and phloem tubes form separate bundles and are found near the centre of the root.

UPTAKE OF WATER BY PLANTS

Water is taken into the plant from the soil. This occurs mainly through the root hairs near the root tip. There are thousands (perhaps millions) of root tips (and root hair regions) on a single healthy crop plant (see Fig. 4).

The absorption of water into the plant in this way is due to a suction pull which starts in the leaves. As water transpires (evaporates) from the cells in the leaf more water is drawn from the xylem tubes which extend from the leaves to the root tips. In these tubes the water is stretched like a taut wire or thread. This is possible because the tiny particles (molecules) of water hold together very firmly when in narrow tubes. The pull of this water in the xylem tubes of the root is transferred through the root cells to the root

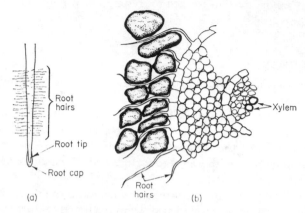

FIG. 4. (a) Section of root tip and root hair region, (b) cross-section of root showing the root hairs as tube-like elongations of the surface cells in contact with soil particles.

hairs and so water is absorbed into the roots and up to the leaves. In general, the greater the rate of transpiration, the greater is the amount of water taken into the plant. The rate of absorption is slowed down by:

(a) shortage of water in the soil,
(b) lack of oxygen for root respiration (e.g. in waterlogged soils),
(c) a high concentration of salts in the soil water near the roots.

Normally, the concentration of the soil solution does not interfere with water absorption. High soil water concentration can occur in salty soils and near bands of fertilizer. Too much fertilizer near developing seedlings may damage germination by restricting the uptake of water.

OSMOSIS

Much of the water movements into and from cell to cell in plants is due to *osmosis*. This is a process in which a solvent, such as water, will flow through a *semi-permeable* membrane (e.g. a cell wall) from a weak solution to a more concentrated one. The cell wall may allow only the water to pass through. The force exerted by such a flow is called the *osmotic pressure*. In plants, the normal movement of the water is into the cell. However, if the concentration of a solution outside the cell is greater than that inside, there is a loss of water from the cell, and its contents contract (shrivel); this is called *plasmolysis*.

### UPTAKE OF NUTRIENTS

The absorption of chemical substances (nutrients) into the root cells is partly due to a *diffusion* process but it is mainly due to ability of the cells near root tips to *accumulate* such nutrients. The process is complicated and not fully understood. It is slowed up if root respiration is checked by a shortage of oxygen.

## Plant Groups

Plants can be divided into annuals, biennials and perennials according to their total length of life.

### ANNUALS

Typical examples are wheat, barley and oats which complete their life history in one growing season, i.e. starting from the seed, in 1 year they develop roots, stem and leaves and then produce flowers and seed before dying.

### BIENNIALS

These plants grow for 2 years. They spend the first year in producing roots, stem and leaves, and the following year in producing the flowering stem and seeds, after which they die.

Sugar-beet, swedes and turnips are typical biennials, although the grower treats these crops as annuals, harvesting them at the end of the first year when all the foodstuff is stored up in the root.

They live for more than 2 years and, once fully developed, they usually produce seeds each year. Many of the grasses and legumes are perennials.

## Structure of the Seed

Plants are also classified as *dicotyledons* and *monocotyledons* according to the structure of the seed.

### DICOTYLEDONS

A good example of a dicotyledon seed is the broad bean because it is large and easy to study. If a pod of the broad bean plant is opened when it is nearly ripe it will be seen that each seed is attached to the inside of the pod by a short stalk called the *funicle*. All the nourishment which the developing seed requires passes through the funicle from the bean plant.

When the seed is ripe and has separated from the pod a black scar, known as the *hilum*, can be seen where the funicle was attached. Near one end of this hilum is a minute hole called the *micropyle* (see Fig. 5).

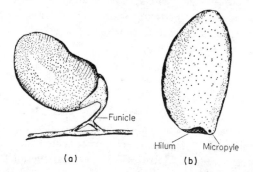

Fig. 5. (a) Bean seed attached to the inside of the pod by the funicle, (b) bean seed showing the hilum and micropyle.

If a bean is soaked in water the seed coat can be removed easily and all that is left is largely made up of the *embryo* (*germ*). This consists of two seed leaves, or *cotyledons*, which contain the food for the young seedling.

Lying between the two cotyledons is the *radicle*, which eventually forms the *primary root*, and a continuation of the radicle the other end, the *plumule* (see Fig. 6). This develops into the young *shoot*, and is the first *bud* of the plant.

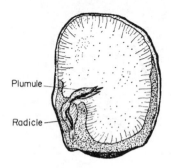

Fig. 6. Bean seed with one cotyledon removed.

## MONOCOTYLEDONS

This class includes all the cereals and grasses and it is, therefore, very important.

The wheat grain is a typical example. It is not a true seed (it should be called a single-seeded fruit). The seed completely fills the whole grain, being practically united with the inside wall of the grain or fruit.

This fruit wall is made up of many different layers which are separated on milling into varying degrees of fineness, e.g. bran and pollards, and these are valuable livestock feed.

Most of the interior of the grain is taken up by the floury *endosperm*. The embryo occupies the small raised area at the base. The *scutellum*, a shield-like structure, separates the embryo from the endosperm. Attached to the base of the scutellum are the five roots of the embryo, one primary and two pairs of *secondary* rootlets. The roots are enclosed by a sheath called the *coleorhiza*. The position of the radicle and the plumule can be seen in the diagram (Fig. 7).

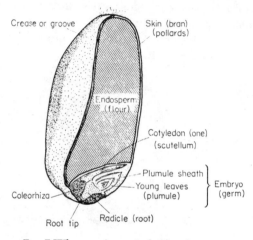

FIG. 7.Wheat grain cut in half at the crease.

The scutellum can be regarded as the cotyledon of the seed. There is only *one* cotyledon present and so wheat is a monocotyledon.

### GERMINATION OF THE BEAN—THE DICOTYLEDON

Given suitable conditions for germination, i.e. water, heat and air, the seed coat of the dormant but living seed splits near the micropyle, and the radicle begins to grow downwards through this split to form the main, or primary root, from which lateral branches will soon develop (see Fig. 8).

When the root is firmly held in the soil, the plumule starts to grow by pushing its way out of the same opening in the seed coat. As it grows upwards its tip is bent to protect it from injury in passing through the soil, but it straightens out on reaching the surface, and *leaves* very quickly develop from the plumular shoot.

With the broad bean the cotyledons remain underground—gradually giving up their stored food materials to the developing plant, but with the French bean, and many other dicotyledon seeds, the cotyledons are brought above ground with the plumule.

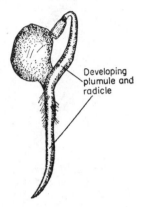

Developing plumule and radicle

FIG. 8. Germination of the bean, one cotyledon removed.

GERMINATION OF WHEAT—THE MONOCOTYLEDON

When the grain germinates the coleorhiza expands and splits open the seed coat, and at the same time the roots break through the coleorhiza (see Fig. 9).

The primary root is soon formed, supported by the two pairs of secondary rootlets, but this root system (the seminal roots) is only temporary and is soon replaced by *adventitious roots* (see Figs. 10 and 14). As the first root system is being formed at the base of the stem so the plumule starts to grow upwards, and its first leaf, the *coleoptile*, appears above the ground as a single pale tube-like structure.

From a slit in the top of the leaf there appears the first *true leaf* which is quickly followed by others, the younger leaves growing from the older leaves (see Fig. 11).

As the wheat embryo grows so the floury endosperm is used up by the developing roots and plumule, and the scutellum has the

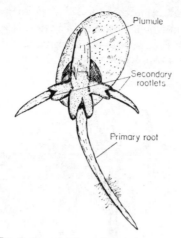

FIG. 9. Germination of the wheat grain.

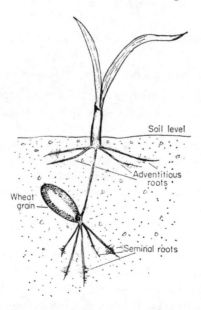

FIG. 10. Developing wheat plant.

important function of changing the endosperm into digestible food for the growing parts.

With the broad bean, the cotyledons provide the food for the early nutrition of the plant, whilst the wheat grain is dependent upon the endosperm and scutellum, and in both cases it is not until the plumule has reached the light and turned green that the plants can begin to be independent.

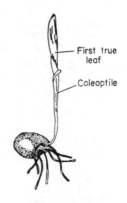

FIG. 11. Seedling wheat plant.

This point is important in relation to the depth at which seeds should be sown. Small seeds, such as the clovers and many of the grasses, must, as far as possible, be sown very shallow. Their food reserves will be exhausted before the shoot reaches the surface if sown too deeply. Larger seeds, such as the beans and peas, can and should be sown deeper.

When the leaves of the plant begin to manufacture food by photosynthesis (see p. 1) and when the primary root has established itself sufficiently well to absorb nutrients from the soil (see p. 7) then the plant can develop independently, provided there is sufficient moisture and air present.

The main differences between the two groups of plants can be summarized as follows:

| *Dicotyledons* | *Monocotyledons* |
|---|---|
| The embryo has two seed leaves. | The embryo has one seed leaf. |
| A primary root system is developed and persists. | A primary root system is developed, but is replaced by an adventitious root system. |
| Usually broad-leafed plants, e.g. clovers, cabbage and potato. | Usually narrow-leaved plants, e.g. the cereals and grasses, and most bulbous plants. |

These two great groups of flowering plants can be further divided in the following way:

| Families or orders e.g. | The legume family, potato, the grasses and cereals. |
|---|---|
| Genus | Clovers of the legume family, and wheat of the cereal family. |
| Species | Red clover. |
| Cultivar or Variety | Broad red clover. |
| Strain | S151 broad red clover. |

### Plant Structure

The plant can be divided into two parts:

### 1. THE ROOT SYSTEM

The root system is concerned with the parts of the plant growing in the soil and there are two main types:

(a) *The tap root or primary system.* This is made up of the primary root called the tap root with *lateral secondary* roots branching out from it, and from these *tertiary* roots may develop obliquely to form, in some cases, a very extensive system of roots (see Fig. 12).

The root of the bean plant is a good example of a tap root system, and if this is split it will be seen that there is a slightly darker central woody core; this is the *skeleton* of the root. It helps to anchor the plant, and also transports foodstuffs. The lateral secondary roots arise from this central core (see Fig. 13).

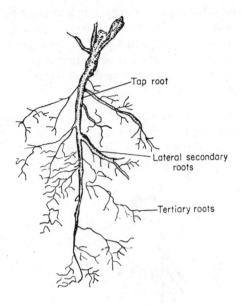

FIG. 12. Tap root or primary root system.

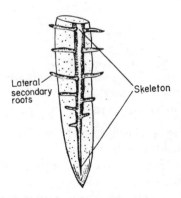

FIG. 13. Tap root of the bean plant.

Carrots, and other true root crops, such as sugar-beet and mangolds, have very well-developed tap roots. These biennials store food in their roots during the first year of growth to be used in the following year for the production of the flowering shoot and seeds. However, they are normally harvested after one season and the roots are used as food for man and stock.

(b) *The adventitious root system.* This is found on all grasses and cereals, and it is, in fact, the main root system of most monocotyledons. The primary root is quickly replaced by adventitious roots, which arise from the base of the stem (see Fig. 14).

Fig. 14. Adventitious root system.

Actually, these roots can develop from any part of the stem, and they are found on some dicotyledons as well, but not as the main root system, e.g. underground stems of the potato.

*Root hairs* (see Fig. 4). These are very small white hair-like structures which are found near the tips of all roots. As the root grows, the hairs on the older parts die off, and others develop on the younger parts of the root.

Root hairs play a very important part in the life of a plant (see p. 5).

## 2. THE STEM

The second part of the flowering plant is the shoot which normally grows upright above the ground. It is made up of a main stem, branches, leaves and flowers.

Stems are either soft (*herbaceous*) or hard (*woody*) and in British agriculture it is only the soft and green herbaceous stems which are of any importance. These usually die back every year.

*How stems grow.* All stems start life as *buds* and the increase in length takes place at the tip of the shoot called the *terminal* bud.

If a Brussels sprout is cut lengthwise and examined, it will be seen that the young leaves arise from the bud *axis*. This axis is made up of different types of cell tissue, which is continually making new cells and thus growing (see Fig. 15).

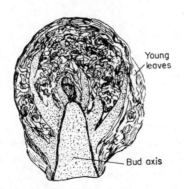

FIG. 15. Longitudinal section of a Brussels sprout.

Stems are usually jointed, each joint forming a *node*, and the part between two nodes is the *internode*. At the nodes the stem is usually solid and thicker, and this swelling is caused by the storing up of material at the base of the leaf (see Fig. 16).

The bud consists of closely packed leaves arising from a number of nodes. It is, in fact, a condensed portion of the stem which develops by a lengthening of the internodes.

*Axillary* buds are formed in the angle between the stem and the leaf stalk. These buds, which are similar to the terminal bud, develop to form lateral *branches*, *leaves* and *flowers*.

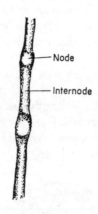

FIG. 16. Jointed stem.

*Some modification of stems*

(1) A *stolon* is a stem which grows along the ground surface. Adventitious roots are produced at the nodes, and buds on the runner can develop into upright shoots, and separate plants can be formed, e.g. strawberry plants (see Fig. 17).

(2) A *rhizome* is similar to a stolon but grows under the surface of the ground, e.g. couch grass (see Fig. 17).

(3) A *tuber* is really a modified rhizome. The end of the rhizomes swell to form tubers. The tuber is therefore a swollen stem. The potato is a well-known example, and it has "eyes" which are really buds and these develop shoots when the potato tuber is planted.

(4) A *tendril* is found on certain legumes, such as the pea. The terminal leaflet is modified as in the diagram. This is useful for climbing purposes to support the plant (see Fig. 18).

*Corms* and *suckers* are other examples of modified stems.

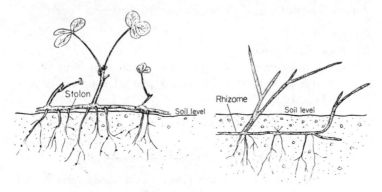

FIG. 17. Modified stems.

FIG. 18. Modified stem.

**THE LEAF**

Leaves in all cases arise from buds. They are extremely important organs, being not only responsible for the manufacture of sugar and starch from the atmosphere for the growing parts of the plant, but they also are the organs through which transpiration of water takes place.

A typical leaf of a dicotyledon consists of three main parts:

(1) The *blade*.
(2) The *stalk* or *petiole*.
(3) The *basal sheath* connecting the leaf to the stem. This may be modified as with legumes into a pair of wing-like *stipules* (see Figs. 19(a), 49–51).

The blade is the most obvious part of the leaf and it is made up of a network of veins.

There are two main types of dicotyledonous leaves:

(1) A prominent central *midrib*, from which lateral veins branch off on either side. These side veins branch into smaller and smaller ones, as in the diagram (see Fig. 19).
(2) No single midrib, but several main ribs spread out from the top of the leaf stalk; between these the finer veins spread out as before, e.g. horse-chestnut leaf (see Fig. 19).

The veins are the essential supply lines for the process of photosynthesis. They consist of two main parts, one for bringing the required raw material up to the leaf (*xylem*), and the other part being concerned with carrying the finished product away from the leaf (*phloem*).

Leaves can show great variation in shape and type of margin, as in Fig. 19. They can also be divided into two broad classes as follows:

(1) *Simple* leaves. The blade consists of one continuous piece (see Fig. 19(a) ).
(2) *Compound* leaves. Simple leaves may become deeply lobed and when the division between the lobes reaches the midrib it is a compound leaf, and the separate parts of the blade are called the *leaflets* (see Fig. 19(b) ).

The blade surface may be *smooth* (glabrous) or *hairy*, according to variety, and this is important in legumes because it can affect its palatability to stock.

Monocotyledonous leaves are dealt with in the section on "Grassland".

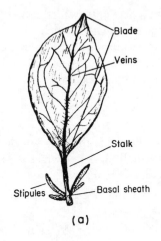

(a)

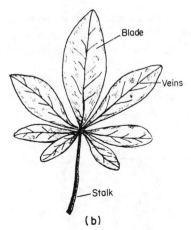

(b)

FIG. 19. (a) Simple leaf, (b) Compound leaf.

*Modified leaves*

(a) *Cotyledons* or seed leaves are usually of a very simple form.

(b) *Scales* are normally rather thin, yellowish to brown membranous leaf structures, very variable in size and form. On woody stems they are present as *bud scales* which protect the bud, and they are also found on rhizomes such as couch.

(c)  *Leaf tendrils.* The terminal leaflet like the stem can be modified into thin threadlike structures, e.g. pea and vetch.

Other examples of modified leaves are *leaf-spines* and *bracts*.


### THE FLOWER

In the centre of the flower is the *axis* which is simply the continuation of the flower stalk. It is known as the *receptacle*, and on it are arranged four kinds of organs:

(1)  The lowermost is a ring of green leaves called the *calyx*, made up of individual *sepals*.

(2)  Immediately above the calyx is a ring of *petals* known as the *corolla*.

(3)  Above the corolla are the *stamens*, again arranged in a ring. They are similar in appearance to an ordinary match, the swollen tip being called the *anther* which, when ripe, contains the *pollen grains*.

(4)  The highest position on the receptacle is occupied by the *pistil* which is made up of one or a series of small green bottle-shaped bodies—the *carpel*, which is itself made up of three parts: the *stigma*, *style*, and the *ovary* (containing *ovules*).

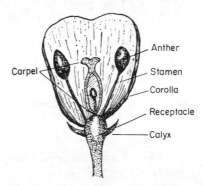

FIG. 20. Longitudinal section of a simple flower.

It is within the ovary that the future *seeds* are produced (see Figs. 20 and 21).

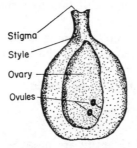

FIG. 21. Carpel.

Most flowers are more complicated in appearance than the above, but basically they consist of these four main parts.

### THE FORMATION OF SEEDS

*Pollination* precedes *fertilization*, which is the union of the male and female reproductive cells. When pollination takes place the pollen grain is transferred from the anther to the stigma. This may be *self-pollination* where the pollen is transferred from the anther to the stigma of the same flower, or *cross-pollination* when it is carried to a different flower (see Fig. 22).

With fertilization the pollen grain grows down the style of the carpel to fuse with the ovule. After fertilization, changes take place

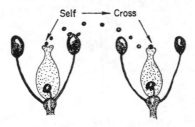

FIG. 22. Self- and cross-pollination.

whereby the ovule develops into the embryo, and endosperm may be formed according to the species. This makes up the *seed*. The ovary also changes after fertilization to form the *fruit*, as distinct from the seed.

With the grasses and cereals there is only one seed formed in the fruit and, being so closely united with the inside wall of the ovary, it cannot easily be separated from it.

The one-seeded fruit is called a *grain*.

### THE INFLORESCENCE

Special branches of the plant are modified to bear the flowers, and they form the inflorescence. There are two main types of inflorescence:

(1) Where the branches bearing the flowers continue to grow, so that the youngest flowers are nearest the apex and the oldest farthest away—*indefinite* inflorescence (see Fig. 23(a) ).

A well known example of this inflorescence is the *spike* found in many species of grasses.

(2) Where the main stem is terminated by a single flower and ceases to grow in length; any further growth takes place by lateral

(a)

FIG. 23. (a) Indefinite inflorescence.

branches, and they eventually terminate in a single flower and growth is stopped—*definite* inflorescence, e.g. stitchworts (see Fig. 23(b) ).

There are many variations of these two main types of inflorescence.

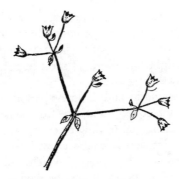

FIG. 23. (b) Definite inflorescence.

### What Plants Need

To grow satisfactorily a plant needs *warmth, light, water, carbon dioxide* and about a dozen other *chemical elements* which it can obtain from the soil.

#### WARMTH

Most crop plants in this country start growing when the average daily temperature is above 6°C (42°F). Growth is best between 16°C (60°F) and 27°C (80°F). These temperatures apply to thermometer readings taken in the shade about 4 ft above ground. Crops grown in hotter countries usually have higher temperature requirements.

Cold frosty conditions may seriously damage plant growth. Crop plants differ in their ability to withstand very cold conditions. For example, winter rye and wheat can stand colder conditions than winter oats. Potato plants and stored tubers are easily damaged by frost. Sugar-beet may bolt (go to seed) if there are frosts after germination; frost in December and January may destroy crops left in the ground.

## LIGHT

Without light, plants cannot produce carbohydrates and will soon die. The amount of photosynthesis which takes place daily in a plant is partly due to the length of daylight and partly to the intensity of the sunlight. Bright sunlight is of most importance where there is dense plant growth.

The lengths of daylight and darkness periods vary according to the distance from the equator and also from season to season. This can affect the flowering and seeding of crop plants and is one of the limiting factors in introducing new crops into a country. Grasses are now being tested in this country which will remain leafy and not produce flowering shoots under the daylight conditions here.

## WATER

Water is an essential part of all plant cells and it is also required in extravagant amounts for the process of transpiration. Water carries nutrients from the soil into and through the plant and also carries the products of photosynthesis from the leaves to wherever they are needed. Plants take up about 200 tons of water for every ton of dry matter produced.

## CARBON DIOXIDE ($CO_2$)

Plants need carbon dioxide for photosynthesis. This is taken into the leaves through the stomata and so the amount which can go in is affected by the rate of transpiration. Another limiting factor is the small amount ($0 \cdot 03\%$) of carbon dioxide in the atmosphere. The percentage can increase just above the surface of soils rich in organic matter where soil bacteria are active and releasing carbon dioxide. This is possibly one of the reasons why crops grow better on such soils.

CHEMICAL ELEMENTS REQUIRED BY PLANTS

In order that a plant may build up its cell structure and function as a food factory many simple chemical substances are needed. These are taken into the roots from the soil solution and the clay particles. Those required in fairly large amounts—a few kilogramme to one or more hundred kilogramme per hectare (a few pounds to one or more hundredweight per acre)—are called the *major* nutrients; those required in small amounts—a few grams to several kilogramme per hectare (part of an ounce to several pounds per acre) —are the *minor* nutrients or *trace elements*.

| The major nutrients | Use | Source |
|---|---|---|
| Carbon (C)<br>Hydrogen (H)<br>Oxygen (O) | Used in making carbohydrates. | The air and water. |
| Nitrogen (N) | Very important for building proteins. | Organic matter (including F.Y.M.). Nodules on legumes (p. 29). Nitrogen fertilizers such as ammonium and nitrate compounds and urea. Nitrogen-fixing soil micro-organisms. |
| Phosphorus (P) (phosphate) | Essential for cell division and many chemical reactions. | Small amounts from the mineral and organic matter in the soil. Mainly from phosphatic fertilizers, e.g. superphosphate, ground rock phosphate, basic slag and compounds, and residues of previous fertilizer applications. |
| Potassium (K) (potash) | Helps with formation of carbohydrates and proteins. Regulates water in and through the plant. | Small amounts from mineral and organic matter in the soil. Potash fertilizers, e.g. muriate and sulphate of potash. |

| The major nutrients | Use | Source |
|---|---|---|
| Calcium (Ca) | Essential for development of growth tissue, e.g. root tips. | Usually enough in the soil. Applied as chalk or limestone to neutralize acidity. |
| Magnesium (Mg) | A necessary part of chlorophyll. | If soil is deficient, may be added as magnesium limestone or magnesium sulphate, also F.Y.M. |
| Sulphur (S) | Part of many proteins and some oils. | Usually enough in the soil. Added in some fertilizers (e.g. sulphate of ammonia and superphosphate). |

The trace elements are:

| | Deficiency symptoms | Remedy |
|---|---|---|
| Boron (B) | *Heart-rot* in sugar-beet and mangolds. *Brown-heart* (*raan*) in turnips and swedes. | 22 kg/ha (20 lb/acre) borax evenly spread, e.g. with fertilizer. |
| Copper (Cu) | Commonest in cereals—leaf tips and edges white-yellowish-grey and in twisted spiral. Head may be distorted or fail to emerge. Yields are very seriously reduced. | 22–56 kg/ha (20–50 lb/acre) of copper sulphate applied to soil to last 3–5 yrs or 1–2 kg/ha ($\frac{3}{4}$–2 lb/acre) copper oxychloride applied to growing crop. |

| | Deficiency symptoms | Remedy |
|---|---|---|
| Copper (*contd.*) | Found on deep fen peats and on black soils of the chalk downs. | |
| Manganese (Mn) | Grey patches on leaves of cereals. "*Marsh-spot*" in peas. *Speckled yellowing* of leaves of sugar-beet. | Manganese sulphate applied to soil ($\frac{1}{2}$–1 cwt/acre) or 10 lb sprayed on young crop, or 14 lb combine drilled (cereals). Some wheat varieties, e.g. Koga II, Rothwell Sprite and Hybrid 46 are resistant to manganese deficiency. |

Deficiencies of boron and manganese are often caused by using too much lime.

Other trace elements are chlorine, iron, molybdenum and zinc, but these rarely cause trouble on most farm soils.

*Cobalt* is not considered necessary for plant growth, but animals feeding on plants deficient in cobalt (e.g. on some all-grass areas) waste away ("pine"). The remedy would be a few pounds of a cobalt salt per acre or in a salt lick.

*Sodium* does not appear to be essential, but some crops such as sugar-beet and mangolds grow better if it is applied (e.g. as common salt). It may partly replace potassium.

The effects of nitrogen, phosphorus and potassium are discussed more fully in the chapter on "Fertilizers".

### Legumes and the Nitrogen Cycle

Legumes are plants which have several interesting characteristics such as:

(1) A special type of fruit called a legume, which splits along both sides to release its seeds, e.g. pea pod.

(2) The flowers closely resemble pea flowers.

(3) Nodules (lumps) on their roots contain special types of bacteria which can "fix" (convert) nitrogen from the air into nitrogen compounds. These bacteria enter the plant through the root hairs from the surrounding soil.

This "fixation" of nitrogen is of considerable agricultural importance. Many of our farm crops are legumes, for example, *peas, beans, vetches, lupins, clovers, lucerne (alfalfa), sainfoin* and *trefoil*. The bacteria obtain carbohydrates (energy) from the plant and in return they supply nitrogen compounds. The nodules can release nitrogen compounds into the soil. These compounds are changed to nitrates and taken up by neighbouring plants (e.g. by grasses in a grass and clover sward) or by the following crop, e.g. wheat after clover or beans. The amount of nitrogen which can be "fixed" by legume bacteria varies widely; estimates of 56–450 kg/ha (50–400 lb/acre) of nitrogen have been made. Some of the reasons for variations are:

(a) *The type of plant.* Some crop plants "fix" more nitrogen than others, e.g. lucerne and clovers (especially if grazed) are usually better than peas and beans.

(b) *The conditions in the soil.* The bacteria usually work best in soils which favour the growth of the plant on which they live.

A good supply of calcium and phosphate in the soil is usually beneficial, although lupins grow well on acid soils.

(c) *The strains of bacteria present.* Most soils in this country contain the strains of bacteria required for most of the leguminous crops which are grown. Lucerne (alfalfa) is an exception and it is common practice to coat the lucerne seed with the proper bacterial culture before sowing; these bacteria will later enter the roots of the young plant.

### The Nitrogen Cycle

The circulation of nitrogen (in various compounds such as nitrates and proteins) as found on the farm is illustrated diagrammatically in Fig. 24.

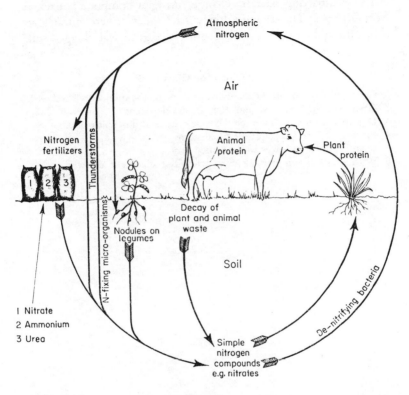

FIG. 24. The nitrogen cycle.

Atmospheric nitrogen is "fixed" (combined) in compounds by *legume nodule bacteria*, by various *nitrogen-fixing micro-organisms*, by *thunderstorms* and in the manufacture of *nitrogen fertilizers*.

Simple nitrogen compounds (mainly nitrates) are taken up by plants to form plant proteins which may then be eaten by animals to form animal proteins. Dead plants and animals, and the faeces and urine of animals are broken down by decay micro-organisms to leave simple nitrogen compounds in the soil.

The denitrifying bacteria change nitrogen compounds back to free nitrogen. This is most likely to happen where nitrates are abundant and oxygen is in short-supply, e.g. in waterlogged soils.

## Suggestions for Classwork

1. Compare and contrast the dicotyledon seed and the monocotyledon seed.
2. Germinate the bean seed, and study its development.
3. Dig up and carefully examine the root system of different plants.
4. Examine different types of modified stems.
5. Examine different leaves and modified leaves.
6. With a magnifying glass, examine carefully the parts of a flower.

# CHAPTER 2

# SOILS

SOILS are very complex natural formations which make up the surface of the earth. They provide a suitable environment in which plants may obtain *water, nutrients, oxygen* for root respiration, and firm *anchorage*. Soils are formed by the weathering of rocks, followed by the growth and decay of plants, animals, and soil micro-organisms. If a farmer is to provide the best possible conditions for crop growth, it is desirable that he should understand what soils are, how they were formed and how they should be managed.

The *topsoil* or *surface soil* is a layer about 80–450 mm (3–18 in.) deep which may be taken as the greatest depth which a farmer would plough or cultivate and in which most of the plant roots are found. Loose, cultivated, top soil is sometimes called *mould*.

The *subsoil*, which lies underneath, is an intermediate stage in the formation of soil from the rock below.

A *soil profile* is a section taken through the soil down to the parent rock. In some cases this may consist of only a shallow surface soil 100–150 mm (4–6 in.) on top of a rock such as chalk or limestone. In other well developed soils (several feet deep) there are usually three or more definite layers (or horizons) which vary in colour, texture and compaction (see Fig. 25).

The soil profile can be examined by digging a trench or by taking out cores of soil from various depths with a *soil auger*.

A careful examination of the layers (horizons) can be useful in forming an opinion as to how the soil was formed, its natural drainage and how it might be farmed. Some detailed soil classifications are based on soil profile.

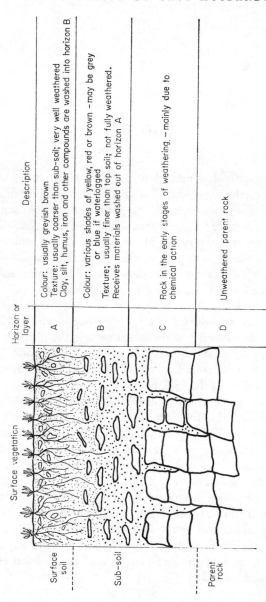

| Horizon or layer | Description |
|---|---|
| A | Colour: usually greyish brown<br>Texture: usually coarser than sub-soil; very well weathered<br>Clay, silt, humus, iron and other compounds are washed into horizon B. |
| B | Colour: various shades of yellow, red or brown – may be grey or blue if waterlogged<br>Texture; usually finer than top soil; not fully weathered.<br>Receives materials washed out of horizon A |
| C | Rock in the early stages of weathering. – mainly due to chemical action |
| D | Unweathered parent rock |

Surface vegetation

Surface soil

Sub-soil

Parent rock

Fig. 25. Soil profile diagram showing the breakdown of rock to form various soil layers (horizons).

## Soil Formation

There are very many different types of soils and subsoils. The differences are mainly due to the variety of rocks from which they are formed. However, other factors such as *climate, topography, plant and animal life,* the *age of the developing soil material* and *farming operations* also affect the type of soil which develops.

### THE MORE IMPORTANT ROCK FORMATIONS

*Igneous or primary rocks,* e.g. *granite* (coarse crystals) and *basalt* (fine crystals). These rocks were formed from the very hot molten material which made up the earth, millions of years ago. The minerals (chemical compounds) in these rocks are mostly in the form of crystals and are the primary source of the minerals found in all our soils. Igneous rocks are very hard and weather very slowly. Clay and sand are break-down products.

*Sedimentary or transported rocks.* These have been formed from weathered material (e.g. clay, silt and sand) carried and deposited by water and wind. The sediments later became compressed by more material on top and cemented to form new rocks such as *sandstones, clays* and *shales.*

The *chalks* and *limestones* were formed from the shells and skeletons of sea animals of various sizes. These rocks are mainly calcium carbonate but in some cases are magnesium carbonate. The calcareous soils are formed from them (see p. 56).

*Metamorphic rocks,* e.g. *marble* (from limestone) and *slate* (from shale). These are rocks which have been changed in various ways.

### ORGANIC MATTER

Deep deposits of *organic matter* (humus) are found in places where waterlogged soil conditions did not allow the breakdown of dead plant material by micro-organisms and oxidation.

Peats have been formed in water-logged acidic areas where the vegetation is mainly mosses, rushes, heather and some trees.

Black fen (muck soil) has been formed in marshy river estuary conditions where the water was hard (lime rich) and often silty; the plants were mainly reeds, sedges, rushes and some trees.

Good drainage is necessary before preparing these areas for cropping.

GLACIAL DRIFT

Many soils in the British Isles are not derived from the rocks underneath but are deposits carried from other rock formations by glaciers, e.g. boulder clays. This makes the study of our soils very complicated.

*Alluvium* is material which has been deposited recently, for example, by river flooding. This material is very variable in composition.

WEATHERING OF ROCKS

The breakdown of rocks is mainly caused by the *physical* and *chemical* effects of the weather.

*Physical weathering.* *Changes of temperature* cause the various mineral crystals in rocks to expand and contract by different amounts, and so cracking and shattering often occurs.

Water can cause pieces of rock surfaces to split off when it freezes and expands in cracks and crevices. Also, the molecules (small particles) of water in the pores and fissures of the rock exert expansion and contraction forces similar to those of freezing and thawing. The pieces of rock broken off are usually sharp-edged, but if they are carried and knocked about by glaciers, rivers or wind, they become more rounded in shape, e.g. sand and stones in a river bed.

*Wetting and drying* of some rocks such as clays and shales causes expansion and contraction and results in cracking and flaking.

*Chemical weathering.* Chemical breakdown of the mineral matter in a developing soil is brought about by the action of water, oxygen, carbon dioxide and nitric acid from the atmosphere; and by carbonic and organic acids from the biological activity in the soil. The soil water, which is a weak acid, dissolves some minerals and allows chemical reactions to take place.

Water can also unite with substances in the soil (hydration) to form new substances which are more bulky and so can cause shattering of rock fragments.

Clay is produced by chemical weathering. In the case of rocks such as granite, when the clay producing parts are weathered away the more resistant quartz crystals are left as sand or silt.

In the later stages of chemical weathering the soil minerals are broken down to release plant nutrients—this is a continuing process in most soils.

### Other Factors in Soil Formation

CLIMATE

The rate of weathering partly depends on the climate. For example, the wide variations in temperature and the high rainfall of the tropics makes for much faster soil development than would be possible in the colder and drier climatic regions.

TOPOGRAPHY

The depth of soil can be considerably affected by the slope of the ground. Weathered soil tends to erode from steep slopes and build up on the flatter land at the bottom. Level land is more likely to produce uniform weathering.

BIOLOGICAL ACTIVITY

Plants, animals and micro-organisms, during their life-cycles, leave many organic substances in the soil. Some of the substances may dissolve some of the mineral material; dead material may partially decompose to give *humus*.

The roots of plants may open up cracks in the soil.

Vegetation such as mosses and lichens can attack and break down the surface of rocks.

Holes made in the soil by burrowing animals such as earthworms, moles, rabbits, etc., help to breakdown soft and partly weathered rocks.

## FARMING OPERATIONS

Deep ploughing and cultivation, artificial drainage, liming, etc., can speed up the soil formation processes very considerably.

## The Physical Make-up of Soil and its Effect on Plant Growth

The farmer must consider the soil from the point of view of its ability to grow crops. To produce good crops the soil must provide suitable conditions in which plant roots can grow. It must also supply nutrients, water and air; and the temperature must be suitable for the growth of the crop.

The soil is composed of:

| | |
|---|---|
| *Solids* | Mainly *mineral matter* (stones, sand, silt, clay, etc.) and *organic matter*—remains of plants and animals. |
| *Liquids* | Mainly *soil water* (a weak acid). |
| *Gases* | *Soil air* (competes with water to occupy the spaces between the particles). |
| *Living organisms* | Micro-organisms such as bacteria, fungi, small soil animals, earthworms, etc. |

## MINERAL MATTER

This weathered material, and especially the clay part, is mainly responsible for making a soil difficult or easy to work. It may provide many plant nutrients—but *not* nitrogen. The farmer normally cannot alter the mineral matter in a soil (but see "*Claying*").

The amounts of clay, silt and sand which a soil contains can be measured by a *mechanical analysis* of a sample in the laboratory (see Table 1, Types of Soil).

## ORGANIC MATTER

Unlike mineral matter, the amount of organic matter in a soil can vary very considerably from time to time. In most fertile soils it is about 3–5% of the dry weight of the soil, but organic soils (e.g. black Fens and peats) consist almost entirely of organic matter. It may remain for a short time in the undecayed state and as such can help to "open-up" the soil—this could be harmful on sandy soils. However, the organic matter is soon attacked by all sorts of soil organisms—bacteria, fungi, earthworms, insects, etc. When they have finished eating and digesting it and each other a complex, dark coloured, structureless material called *humus* remains: materials produced during the breakdown process are very beneficial in restoring and stabilizing a good soil structure.

The amount of humus formed is greatest from plants which have a lot of strengthening (lignified) tissue (e.g. straw). Humus is finally broken down by an oxidation process which is not fully understood.

The amount of humus which can remain in a soil is fairly constant for any particular type of soil. The addition of more organic matter often does not alter the humus content appreciably because the rate of breakdown increases. Organic matter is broken down most rapidly in warm, moist soils which are well limed and well aerated. Break down is slowest in waterlogged, acid conditions.

The chemical make-up of humus is not fully understood but its effects on the soil are well-known.

Like clay, it is a *colloid* (i.e. it is a gluey substance which behaves like a sponge—it absorbs water and swells up when wetted and shrinks on drying). The humus colloids are not so gummy and plastic as the clay colloids but they can improve light (sandy) soils by binding groups of particles together. This reduces the size of the pores (spaces between the particles) and increases the water-holding capacity. Humus can also improve clay soils by making them less plastic and by assisting in the formation of a crumb structure— lime must also be present. Earthworms help in this soil improvement by digesting the clay and humus material with lime.

Plant nutrients—particularly nitrogen and phosphorus—are released for uptake by other plants when organic matter breaks down. The humus colloids can hold bases such as potassium and ammonia in an available form. In these ways it has a very beneficial effect in promoting steady crop growth.

Organic matter in the soil may be maintained or increased by growing *leys*, working-in *straw* and similar *crop residues*, *farmyard manure*, *composts*, etc. The roots and stubble are usually sufficient to maintain an adequate humus content in a soil growing cereals continuously.

In areas where erosion by wind and water is common, mineral soils are less likely to suffer damage if they are well supplied with humus.

Where it is possible to grow good leys and utilize them fully, this is one of the best ways of maintaining a high level of organic matter and a good soil structure.

Increasing the organic matter (humus) content of a soil is the best way of increasing its water holding capacity: 50–60 t/ha (20–25 tons/acre) of well-rotted F.Y.M. may increase the amount of water which can be held by 25% or more.

### Water in the Soil

Soils vary in their capacity to hold water, and to understand why, it is necessary to understand some of the differences between soils.

The soil is a mass of irregular-shaped particles forming a network of spaces or channels called the *pore space*, which may be filled with air or water or both. If the pore space is completely filled with water the soil is *waterlogged* and unsuitable for plant growth because the roots need oxygen for respiration. Ideally, there should be about equal volumes of air and water.

When the soil particles are small (e.g. clay) then the spaces between the particles are also small; and when they are large (e.g. sand) the spaces are large. However, although the spaces are small in a clay soil there are very many more spaces than in the same volume of a sandy soil. In a clay soil about half of the total volume is pore space whereas in a sandy soil only about one third is pore space. These volumes refer to dry soils. The pore space may be altered by a change in:

(a) grouping of the soil particles (i.e. structure),
(b) amount of organic matter (humus) present,
(c) compaction of the soil.

The fact that clay soils have a greater pore space than sandy soils partly explains why the clay soil can hold more water.

Another important factor is the *surface area* of the particles.

Water is held as a thin layer or film around the soil particles. The smaller the particles the stronger are the attractive forces holding the water. Also, the smaller the particles the greater is the surface area per unit volume. (Compare boxes filled with billiard balls, marbles and small ball-bearings.) A comparison for pure materials is set out below.

| Material | Particle size (mm) | Surface area |
|---|---|---|
| Coarse sand | 2·0 | × |
| Finest sand | 0·02 | 100 × |
| Finest silt | 0·002 | 1,000 × |
| Finest clay | | 100,000 × |

The surface area of the particles in a cubic foot of fine clay may be over 100 acres.

The organic matter (humus) in the soil also holds water.

The water in the soil comes from rainfall, or, in dry areas, from irrigation.

When water falls on a dry soil it does *not* become evenly distributed through the soil. The topmost layer becomes saturated first and as more water is added the depth of the saturated layer increases. In this layer most of the pore space is filled with water. However, a well-drained soil cannot hold all of this water for very long. After a day or so some of the water will soak into the lower layers or run away in drains. The amount of water which is then retained by the soil is called the *moisture-holding capacity* or *field capacity*. The amount of water which can be held in this way varies according to the texture, and structure of the soil (see pp. 47 and 74). The weight of water held by a clay soil may be equal to the weight of the soil particles, whereas a sandy soil may hold less than one-tenth of the weight of the particles. The water-holding capacity of a soil is usually expressed in inches, e.g. a clay soil may have a field capacity of 4 mm/cm (5 in./ft) in depth.

The ways in which water is retained in the soil can be summarized as follows:

(a) as a film around the soil particles,
(b) in the organic matter,
(c) filling some of the smaller spaces,
(d) chemically combined with the soil minerals.

Most of this water can be easily taken up by plant roots but as the soil dries out the remaining water is more firmly held and eventually a stage is reached when no more water can be extracted by the plant. This is called the *wilting point* because plants wilt permanently and soon die. This *permanent wilting* should not be confused with the *temporary wilting* which sometimes occurs on very hot days because the rate of transpiration is greater than the rate of water absorption through the roots; in these cases the plants recover during the night or earlier. The water which can be taken up by the plant roots is called the *available water*. It is the difference between the amounts at field capacity and wilting point. In clay soils only about 50–60% of "field capacity" water is available; in sandy soils up to 90% or more may be available. Although plants may not die until the wilting point is reached, they will suffer from shortage of water as it becomes more difficult to extract (see Fig. 26).

Water in the soil tends to hold the particles together and lumps of soil may stick together. When a loam or heavy soil is at or above half field capacity it is possible to form it into a ball which will not fall apart when handled and tossed about. At wilting point, the soil is crumbly and will not hold together. So, if irrigation is economically possible, it should be used before the soil dries out to a state in which it will not hold together.

Some of the water in soils with very small pores and channels can move through the soil by *capillary forces*, i.e. surface tension between the water and the walls of the fine tubes or capillaries. This is a very slow movement and may not be fast enough to supply plant roots in a soil which is drying out. Heavy rolling of a soil may reduce the size of the pores and so set up some capillary action.

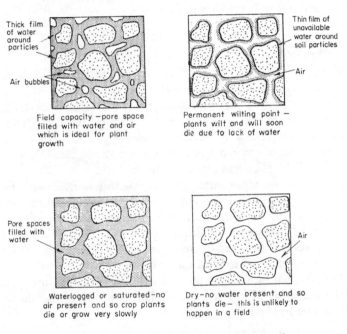

Field capacity —pore space filled with water and air which is ideal for plant growth

Permanent wilting point — plants wilt and will soon die due to lack of water

Waterlogged or saturated—no air present and so crop plants die or grow very slowly

Dry—no water present and so plants die— this is unlikely to happen in a field

Fig. 26. Highly magnified particles and pores showing how water and air may be found in the soil.

Water is lost from the soil by *evaporation* from the surface and by *transpiration* through plants. It moves very slowly from the body of the soil to the surface, so after the top 20 to 50 mm (1–2 in.) have dried out the loss of water by evaporation is very small. Cultivations increase evaporation losses. Most of the available water in a soil is taken up by plants—during the growing season—and air moves in to take its place. This movement of air is easy where the soil has large pore spaces but the movement into the very small pore channels in clay soils is slow until the soil shrinks and cracks—vertically and horizontally—as the water is removed by plants.

The water which enters the soil soon becomes a dilute solution of the soluble soil chemicals. It dissolves some of the carbon dioxide in the soil and so becomes a weak acid.

## SOIL AERATION

Plant roots and many of the soil animals and micro-organisms require oxygen for respiration and give out carbon-dioxide. The air found in the soil is really atmospheric air which has been changed by these activities (and also by various chemical reactions), and so contains less oxygen and much more carbon dioxide. After a time this reduction in oxygen and increase in carbon dioxide becomes harmful to the plant and other organisms.

*Aeration* is the replacement of this stagnant soil air with fresh air. The process is mainly brought about by the movement of water into and out of the soil, e.g. rain water soaks into the soil filling many of the pore spaces and driving out the air. Then, as the surplus water soaks down to the drains or is taken up by plants, fresh air is drawn into the soil to refill the pore spaces.

Also, oxygen moves into the soil and carbon dioxide moves out of the soil by a diffusion process similar to what happens through the stomata in plant leaves.

The aeration process is also assisted by:

(1) changes in temperature,
(2) changes in barometric pressure,
(3) good drainage,
(4) cultivations—especially on clay soils and where a soil cap has formed,
(5) open soil structure.

Sandy soils are usually well aerated because of their open structure.

Clay soils are usually poorly aerated—especially when the very small pores in such soils become filled with water. Good aeration is especially important for germinating seeds and seedling plants.

SOIL MICRO-ORGANISMS

There are thousands of millions of very small organisms in every ounce of fertile soil. Many different types are found but the main groups are:

(1) *Bacteria*—the most numerous group. Bacteria are the smallest type of single-celled organisms and can only be seen with a microscope. There are many kinds in the soil. Most of them feed on and break down organic matter. They obtain energy from the carbohydrates (e.g. sugar, starches, cellulose, etc.) and release carbon dioxide in the process. They also need nitrogen to build cell proteins. If they cannot get this protein from the organic matter they may use other sources such as the nitrogen applied as fertilizers. When this happens (e.g. where straw is ploughed in) the following crop may suffer from shortage of nitrogen unless extra fertilizer is applied. Some types of bacteria can convert (fix) the nitrogen from the air into nitrogen compounds which can be used by plants (see Legumes and the Nitrogen Cycle, p. 29). Soil bacteria are most active in warm, damp, well aerated soils which are not acid.

(2) *Fungi*. Fungi are simple types of plants which feed on and break down organic matter. They are mainly responsible for breaking down lignified (woody) tissue. They have *no* chlorophyll or proper flowers. The fungi usually found in arable soils are very small, but larger types are found in other soils, e.g. peats. Fungi can live in acid conditions and in drier conditions than bacteria. (Mushrooms are fungi, and "fairy rings" are produced by fungi.) Sometimes disease-producing fungi develop in some fields, e.g. those causing "take-all" and "eyespot" in cereals.

(3) *Actinomycetes*. These are organisms which are intermediate between bacteria and fungi and have a similar effect on the soil. They need oxygen for growth and are more common in the drier, warmer soils. They are not so numerous as bacteria and fungi. Some

types can cause plant diseases, e.g. common scab in potatoes (worst in light, dry soils).

(4) *Algae.* Soil algae are very small simple organisms which contain chlorophyll and so can build up their bodies by using carbon dioxide from the air and nitrogen from the soil. Algae grow well in fertile damp soils exposed to the sun. Algae growing in swampy (waterlogged) soils can use dissolved carbon dioxide from the water and release oxygen. This process is an important source of oxygen for crop plants such as rice. Algae are important in colonizing bare soils in the early stages of weathering.

(5) *Protozoa.* These are very small, single-celled animals. Most of them feed on bacteria and similar small organisms. A few types contain chlorophyll and so can produce carbohydrates like plants.

The activities of the micro-organisms in the soil are rather complex and as yet not fully understood, but we do know that they improve the productivity of the soil. In general, the more fertile the soil the more organisms there are present.

### EARTHWORMS

It is generally believed that earthworms have a beneficial effect on the fertility of soils, particularly those under grass, but there is very little definite proof that they do any good on arable land. There are several different kinds found in our soils but most of their activities are very similar. They live in holes in the soil and feed on organic matter—either living plants or, more often, dead and decaying matter. They carry down into the soil fallen leaves and twigs, straw, and similar materials. Earthworms do not thrive in acid soils because they want plenty of calcium (lime) to digest with the organic matter they eat. Their casts, which are usually left on the surface, consist of a useful mixture of organic matter, mineral matter and lime. This material may weigh 25 tonne/ha (10 tons/ acre). The greatest numbers are found in loam soils (under grass) where there is usually a good supply of air, moisture, organic matter and lime. Various methods have been tried to estimate the numbers present in a soil but with limited success.

The many holes they make allow water to enter and drain from the soil very easily and this in turn draws fresh air in as it soaks downwards. This may not always be a good thing, because the holes often have a smooth and, in places, impervious lining which may allow the water to go through to the drains too easily instead of soaking into the soil.

Earthworms are the main food of the mole which does so much damage by burrowing and throwing up heaps of soil.

OTHER SOIL ANIMALS

In addition to earthworms there are many species of small animals present in most soils. They feed on living and decaying plant material and micro-organisms. Some of the common ones are: slugs, snails, millipedes, centipedes, ants, spiders, eelworms, beetles, larvae of various insects such as cutworms, leather jackets and wireworms. The farmer is only directly concerned with those which damage his crops or livestock. The more troublesome crop pests are dealt with in Chapter 7.

## Soil Texture and Structure

*Soil texture* is that characteristic which is determined by the amounts of clay, silt, sand and organic matter which the soil contains. This property normally cannot be altered by the farmer (but see "Claying"). Soil texture can be measured by a *mechanical analysis* of a sample in the laboratory and classified accordingly. (See Table 1, "Types of soil".)

*Soil structure* is the arrangement of the soil particles individually (e.g. grains of sand), in groups (e.g. crumbs or clods) or as a mixture of the two. It can be altered by: *weather conditions* (e.g. lumps changed to crumbs by frost action or alternate wetting and drying), *penetration of plant roots*, *cultivations*, etc. It is not possible to measure soil structure satisfactorily.

"Field texture" is the combined effect of texture and structure at any one time and can be assessed by the "feel" of a moist handful of the soil when rubbed between the fingers.

Clay is sticky, can be moulded, and will take a polish.
Silt feels silky, smooth and slightly sticky.
Sand feels gritty.
Organic matter usually feels soft and slightly sticky.

It is possible to classify the soil according to which "feeling" is dominant; if none is dominant then the soil is a loam. A skilled person may classify up to ten textures by this practical method.

The names commonly used to classify soils in this way are heavy or light, clayey, loamy or sandy. The terms "heavy" and "light" refer to the amount of power required to draw a plough or cultivator through the soil. A heavy (clayey) soil consists mainly of very small particles which pack tightly together whereas a light (sandy) soil consists mainly of large particles which are loosely held together because of the relatively large pore spaces.

Crumb structure is formed by the grouping together (aggregation) of the particles of clay, sand and silt. This aggregation is possible because there are positive and negative electric charges (forces) acting through the surface of the particles. These forces are strongest in clay and very weak in sand. This strong adhesive property of clay particles makes clay soils more difficult to work than sandy soils but it also enables them to form crumbs easily.

Water has special electric properties and its presence is necessary for the grouping (crumbing) of soil particles. The electric forces in the water and in the soil particles make the water stick as a thin film around the particles of soil. As this film becomes thinner (e.g. when soil is drying out) the particles are drawn closer together to form groups (crumbs). The particles in the crumbs may come apart again if the soil becomes very wet.

There must be lime present in the water if clay particles are to stick together to form porous crumbs. This partly explains why liming benefits clay soils.

If organic matter or an iron compound (ferric hydroxide) is present then the particles in the crumbs may remain cemented together and have a more lasting effect on soil structure. Too much ferric hydroxide can have a harmful effect because tightly cemented crumbs are very difficult to wet again after they have dried out. This condition occurs in the so-called "drummy" soils found in the fen district.

Where there is very little organic matter or ferric hydroxide the stability of the crumbs depends mainly on the amount of clay present. The more clay there is, the stronger will be the forces holding the particles together.

Some soil structures are more stable than others, e.g. clays usually have a more stable structure than silts. Soils containing fine sand and silt easily lose their structure and are difficult to work if they are low in organic matter. This is because under wet conditions the sand and silty materials flow very easily and block the aeration and drainage channels in the soil.

*Tilth* is a term used to describe the condition of the soil in a seed-bed. For example, the soil may be in a finely divided state or it may be rough and lumpy; also, the soil may be damp or it may be very dry. Whether a tilth is suitable or not partly depends on the crop to be grown. In general, small seeds require a finer tilth than large seeds.

## Soil Fertility and Productivity

Soil fertility is a rather loose term used to indicate the potential capacity of a soil to grow a crop (or sequence of crops). The productivity of a soil is the combined result of fertility and management.

The fertility of a soil at any one time is partly due to its natural make-up (inherent or *natural fertility*) and partly due to its *condition* (variable fertility) at that time.

*Natural fertility* has an important influence on the *rental* and *sale value* of land. It is the result of factors which are normally beyond the control of the farmer, such as:

(1) the texture and chemical composition of the mineral matter,
(2) the topography (natural slope of the land)—this can affect drainage, temperature and workability of the soil,
(3) climate and local weather—particularly the effects on temperature, and rainfall (quantity and distribution).

*Soil condition* is largely dependent on the management of the soil in recent times. It can be built up by good husbandry but if this high standard is not maintained the soil will soon return to its natural fertility level. The application of fertilizers can raise soil fertility by increasing the quantities of plant food in the growth and decay cycle.

*Management* can control the following production factors:

(1) the amount of organic matter in the soil (see "Soils"),
(2) artificial drainage and irrigation (see "Soil Improvement"),
(3) erosion (removal of soil by wind and water) (see "Claying"),
(4) pH of the soil (see "Liming"), and the plant nutrients applied (see "Fertilizers" and "Crops"),
(5) cultivations and time of planting (see "Cultivations"),
(6) variety and plant spacing (see individual crops),
(7) sequence of cropping (see "Rotations"),
(8) weeds, pests and diseases (see separate chapters).

Good management of the above factors should maintain or increase soil fertility and at the same time be commercially profitable. These subjects are dealt with in more detail in other chapters.

## Types of Soil

There are wide variations in the types of soil found on farms. They may be classified in various ways but here they are grouped according to texture. The amount of clay, silt and sand which they contain can be found by a mechanical analysis. This is an elaborate separation of the particles by settling from a water suspension and sieving in the laboratory which can give accurate measurements of the amount of sand, silt and clay particles present. Gravel and stones are not included in a sample for mechanical analysis. The generally accepted size of particles for each material is given in Table 1.

The "farm-soil" groups to be considered in more detail are: *Clay, sand, loam, silt, calcareous, peat* and *black fen*.

The approximate mechanical analyses of some soil types are shown in Table 2.

TABLE 1

| Material | Diameter of particles |
|----------|----------------------|
| Clay | less than 0·002 mm |
| Silt | 0·02–0·002 mm |
| Fine sand | 0·2–0·02 mm |
| Coarse sand | 2·0–0·2  mm |
| Gravel | more than 2·0 mm |

TABLE 2. TEXTURAL GROUPING OF SOILS (ON DRY WEIGHT)

| Soil type | Texture | Clay (%) | Silt (%) | Sand (%) |
|-----------|---------|----------|----------|----------|
| Clay | Fine (heavy) | over 50 | 15–25 | up to 35 |
| Clay loam | Fine (heavy) | 30–50 | 15–25 | 35–45 |
| Silt loam | Medium | 20–30 | 30–50 | 30–35 |
| Loam | Medium | 20–30 | 20–30 | about 50 |
| Sandy loam | Coarse (light) | 10–20 | 15–25 | 55–75 |
| Sand | Coarse (light) | 0–10 | 0–10 | 80–100 |

A given amount of clay has a very much greater effect on the characteristics of a soil than the same amount of sand or silt.

CLAY SOILS

These soils have a high proportion of clay and silty material—usually over 60%; of this, at least half is *pure clay*, which is mainly responsible for their characteristic qualities. The particles of pure clay are so small that they cannot be seen under an ordinary microscope but they have several very important *colloidal* and base-exchange properties. e.g.

They are gluey and plastic (can be moulded).
They will *swell* when wetted and *shrink* when dried.

They can group together into small clusters (flocculate) or become scattered (deflocculated).

They can combine with various chemical substances (base-exchange) such as calcium, sodium, potassium and ammonia and in this way may hold plant nutrients in the soil.

Grouping or flocculation of the particles is very important in making clay soils easy to work. Clay particles combined with calcium (lime) will flocculate easily whereas those combined with sodium will not and so salt (sodium chloride) must be used very carefully on clay soils. Deflocculation can occur when clays are worked in a wet condition. The adhesive properties of clay are very beneficial to the soil structure when the groups of particles are small (like crumbs) but can be very harmful when large lumps (clods) are formed. Frost action, and alternating periods of wetting and drying will help to restore them to the flocculated crumb condition.

*Characteristics*

(1) Clay soils feel very *sticky* when wet and can be moulded into various shapes.

(2) They can hold more total water than most other soil types and although only about half of this is available to plants, crops seldom suffer from drought.

(3) They *lie wet in winter* so stock should be taken off the land to avoid *poaching*.

(4) They are very *late* in warming up in springtime because water heats up much slower than mineral matter.

(5) They are normally fairly *rich in potash*, but are deficient in phosphates.

(6) Lime requirements are very variable—a clay soil which is well limed usually has a better structure and so is easier to work; over-liming will not cause any troubles such as trace-element deficiency.

*Management.* They should not be worked in spring when wet because they become puddled and later dry into hard lumps, which can only be broken down by well timed cultivations following repeated wetting (swelling) and drying (shrinking). Some air is drawn into cracks caused by shrinkage, and remains when the clod is wetted again and so lines of weakness are formed which eventually allow the clod to be broken. In dry weather irrigation may be used to wet the clods.

In prolonged dry weather, wide and deep cracks are formed which may break animals' legs but which are very beneficial for drainage later.

Clays are often called *heavy* soils because, compared with light (sandy) soils, for ploughing and cultivating two to four times the amount of tractor power is required. All cultivations must be very carefully timed (often restricted to a short period) so that the soil structure is not damaged. This means that more tractors and implements are required than on similar sized loam or sandy soil farms. Autumn ploughing, to allow for a frost tilth, is essential if good seed-beds are to be produced in the spring.

Good drainage is essential. Many clay fields are still in "ridge-and-furrow". This was set up by ploughing—making the "openings" and "finishes" in the same respective places until a distinct ridge and furrow pattern was formed. The direction of the furrows is the same as the fall on the field so that water can easily run off into ditches. This practice also increases the grazing area of a field and for this reason is sometimes found on other types of soil! If these ridges and furrows are levelled out then a mole-drainage system using tiled main drains should be substituted (see "Drainage"). This change is well worthwhile where arable crops are grown.

In many clay-land areas—especially where rainfall is high—the fields are often small and irregular in shape because the boundaries were originally ditches which followed the fall of the land. The hedges and deciduous trees, which were planted later, grow very well on these fertile, wet soils.

The close texture and an adequate water supply often restrict root development on clay soils.

Organic matter, such as strawy farmyard manure, ploughed-in straw or grassland residues make these soils easier to work.

*Cropping.* Because of the many difficulties to be overcome in growing arable crops on these soils they are often left in *permanent grass* and only grazed during the growing season. Where arable crops are grown, a 3- or 4-year ley is often included in the rotation. *Winter wheat* is the most popular arable crop; *winter beans* are also grown in some areas. Both these crops are planted in the autumn (preferably October) when more liberties can be taken with seed-bed preparation than would be permissible in the springtime. *Mangolds* and *cabbage* grow well on clay soils but are declining in popularity in many areas. *Sugar-beet* and *potatoes* are grown in some districts but are very troublesome because of the difficulties in seed-bed preparation, weed control and harvesting—especially in a wet autumn. The best place to take either of these crops is after a period under grass when the soil structure is more stable and the soil easier to work.

SANDY SOILS

*Characteristics*

(1) In many ways these are the opposite of clays and are often called *light* soils because comparatively little power is required to draw cultivation implements.

(2) They can be worked at any time—even in wet weather— without harmful effects.

(3) They are normally free-draining but a few drains may be required where there is clay or other impervious layer underneath.

(4) They have a high proportion of sand and other coarse particles but very little clay—usually less than 5%—(they feel gritty).

(5) They warm up early in spring but crops are very liable to "burn-up" in a dry period because the water holding capacity is low.

*Management.* Sandy soils are naturally very low in plant nutrients and fertilizers are easily washed out, so adequate amounts of fertilizer must be applied to every crop. *Liming* is necessary but must be used carefully—a little and often is the rule here.

Organic matter—especially as *humus*—is very beneficial because it helps to hold water and plant nutrients in the soil. On properly limed fields it breaks down very rapidly because the soil micro-organisms are very active in these open-textured soils which have a good air supply.

*Irrigation* can be very important if the rainfall is low or not well distributed over the growing season.

In some sandy areas the surface soil is liable to "blow" in dry, windy weather and so could destroy a young crop. Where possible, the remedy is to add about 400 t/ha (160 tons/acre) of clay (see "Claying"). Shelter belts are helpful where clay is not readily available.

*Cropping.* A wide range of crops can be grown but yields are very dependent on a good supply of water and adequate fertilizers. *Market gardening* is often carried on where a good sandy area is situated near a large population; e.g. Sandy, Potton, Biggleswade area (Beds.). Here growers are prepared to use irrigation and apply plenty of manures and fertilizers on these *very early, easily worked soils*.

On the lighter sands in low rainfall areas and where irrigation is not possible, the main crops grown are *rye, carrots, sugar-beet*, and *lucerne; lupins* are grown in a few areas where the soil is very poor and acid.

On the better sandy soils, and particularly where the water supply (from rain or irrigation) is reasonably good, the main arable farm-crops grown are *barley, peas, rye, sugar-beet, potatoes* and *carrots*.

Because of the poor quality of this type of land the farms and fields are usually larger than on better-land farms. Hedges are not very common because there is not enough water for good growth. The trees are usually drought-resistant coniferous types.

Stock can be out-wintered on sandy soils with very little risk of damage by poaching even in wet weather.

LOAMS

*Characteristics*

(1) These are intermediate in texture between the clays and sandy soils and, in general, have most of the advantages and few of the disadvantages of these two extreme types. They may feel gritty but also somewhat sticky.

(2) The amount of clay present varies considerably and so this group is sometimes divided into *heavy* or *clay loams* (resembling clays in many respects), *medium loams* and *sandy* or *light loams* (resembling the better sandy soils).

(3) These soils warm up reasonably early in spring and are fairly resistant to drought.

*Management.* Loams are easily worked but should not be worked when wet—especially clay loams. They usually require to be drained but this is not difficult using tile or plastic drains.

*Cropping.* They are regarded by most farmers as the *best all-round soils* because they are naturally fertile and can be used for growing any crop provided the depth of soil is sufficient. Crop yields do not vary much from year to year.

Farms with loamy soils can be used for most types of arable or grassland farming but in general, mixed farming is carried on. Cereals, potatoes and sugar-beet are the main cash crops and leys provide grazing and winter bulk foods for dairy cows, beef cattle or sheep.

CALCAREOUS SOILS

*Characteristics.* These are soils derived from *chalk* and *limestone* rocks and contain various amounts of calcium carbonate—usually 5-50%. The depth of soil and subsoil may vary from 80 mm (3 in.) to over a metre (3 ft). In general, the deep soils are more fertile than the shallow ones. The ease of working and stickiness of these soils depends on the amount of clay and chalk or limestone present; they usually have a loamy texture. Sharp-edged *flints* of various sizes, found in soils over-lying some of the chalk formations, are very wearing on cultivation implements and rubber tyres, and are rather destructive when picked up by harvesting machinery. In some places the flints are found mixed with clay, e.g. *clay-with-flints* soils.

The soils are free-draining except in a few small areas where there is a deep clayish subsoil. Dry valleys are characteristic of these downlands and wolds. The few rivers rise from underground streams.

There are very few hedges and most of the trees have been planted for various reasons—they are mainly beech and conifers.

Walls of local stone form the field boundaries in some limestone areas, e.g. the Cotswolds.

*Management.* The soils are usually deficient in phosphates and potash but only the deeper ones are likely to need liming (see "Liming"). Organic matter can be beneficial but it breaks down fairly rapidly and may be expensive to replace.

The farms and fields on this type of land are usually large— especially on the thinner soils.

Some areas are still unfenced and have no water laid on for stock but this state of affairs is changing as mixed farming systems with grazing animals replace the folded-sheep flocks.

The flooding of water-meadows used to be a common practice but is not done now because labour costs are too high.

CROPPING

*Barley* and *wheat* (on the deeper soils) are the best crops for these soils. The combine-drill for sowing cereals has been very useful in producing good crops—particularly on the poorer, thinner soils. Continuous barley growing is now common on many farms and is likely to become a widely accepted practice. Roots, such as *sugar-beet* and *mangolds*, and *potatoes* are grown on some of the deeper soils. *Leys* for grazing and seed production provide a rotational break with cereal growing. *Kale* is grown on some farms for stock, and pheasant cover! Apart from some parkland, only the poorest, thinnest soils remain as permanent grassland.

SILTS

*Characteristics.* These are soils which contain a high proportion of silt (up to 80% or more). The particles (between clay and sand in size) pack together very closely and retard the movement of water.

*Bad drainage* is one of the main problems with these soils. They do not have a stable subsoil structure such as is found in clay soils. The particles do not group together readily and firmly and so quickly block up drainage cracks and tile drains. Unlike clay, the silt particles cannot take part in chemical reactions so adding lime is not helpful; it is very difficult to create an easy-working soil structure. Frost has very little useful effect.

*Management and cropping.* Arable cropping is very difficult and these areas are best left down to permanent grass. Deep-rooted plants, such as *lucerne*, left growing for several years, are likely to be helpful in opening up the subsoil with their roots and so facilitating drainage.

There is not much land of this type in the British Isles—the best example is part of the Lower Weald in Sussex.

*Note.* The Fenland "silts" are alluvial material consisting mainly of clay, silt and fine sand. They vary in texture from sandy to medium loam. These soils are very fertile and fairly easy to work. They are cropped intensively with all kinds of arable crops—the main ones are *wheat, potatoes, sugar-beet, peas, seed production from root crops and grasses, bulbs* and *market gardening crops.*

PEATS AND PEATY SOILS

*Characteristics.* Peaty soils contain about 20–25% of organic matter whereas there is about 50–90% in true peats.

The *acid* or *peat-bog* peats and peaty soils have been formed in waterlogged areas where plants such as mosses, cotton grass, heather, molinia and rushes grew. The dead material from these plants was only partly broken down by the types of bacteria which can survive under these acidic waterlogged conditions. This "humus" material built up slowly—probably a foot or so every century.

When reclaimed, these soils break down easily to release nutrients, particularly nitrogen, but they are very low in phosphates and potash. Old tree trunks have to be dug out from time to time as the level of the soil falls due to organic matter breakdown.

*Management.* Before reclaiming this land for cropping, much of the peat is often cut away for fuel or sold as peat moss for horticultural purposes or bedding. Good drainage must then be carried out by cutting deep ditches through the area. Deep ploughing also helps to drain the soil. Heavy applications—up to 25 t/ha (10 tons/acre)—of ground limestone may be required to neutralize the acidity.

In the first year, about 15 t/ha (6 tons/acre) of farmyard manure improves the yields of pioneer crops (usually potatoes, sometimes oats or rye); the reason for this may be that the F.Y.M. introduces beneficial types of bacteria.

*Cropping.* In exposed areas they are often sown down to good grasses and clovers. Good swards can be established but these must not be over-grazed or "poached" in wet weather otherwise the field will quickly go back to rushes and weed grasses. Under cultivation, most arable crops can be grown but potatoes and oats are the most suitable.

BLACK FEN SOILS

*Characteristics.* Black Fen soils are found in part of the Fen district of East Anglia and are amongst the most fertile soils in the British Isles. (The "muck soils" of North America are somewhat similar.)

These soils were formed in marshy river estuary conditions where the water came from limestone and chalk areas and so carried calcium carbonate and, in flood times, considerable amounts of silty material. The remains of the vegetation (mainly reeds, sedges and other estuary plants) did not break down completely because of the waterlogged conditions and so built up as humus. The soils vary a lot from district to district but most of them consist almost entirely of organic matter.

*Management.* After building strong sea walls, the area has been reclaimed by draining with deep ditches and underground drains. Most of the land is below sea level and so the water in the ditches has to be pumped over the sea walls or into the main drainage channels.

The soil breaks down readily and the level is falling about 1 in. per year and eventually will reach the clay or gravel subsoil. Tree trunks have to be dug out occasionally.

"Blowing" in spring is a serious problem on these dry, sooty black, friable soils. Several plantings of crop seedlings together with the top 2 or 3 in. of soil and fertilizers may be blown into the ditches. This can be prevented by applying 400–750 tonne of clay per hectare (160–300 tons/acre) (see "Claying"), or by deep ploughing or cultivation 1–1·5 metres (3–5 ft deep) to mix the underlying clay and organic top soil.

These soils are rich in nitrogen, released by the breakdown of the organic matter, but are very poor in phosphates and potash and also trace elements such as manganese and copper.

*Cropping.* This is an intensive arable area where the main crops are *wheat, potatoes* and *sugar-beet*; also smaller acreages of *celery, peas, carrots* and market garden crops.

In some parts leys have been introduced—with limited success—in an attempt to check the rapid rate of breakdown of the soils.

### Soil Improvement

#### 1. LIMING

Most farm crops will not grow satisfactorily if the soil is very acid (sour). This can be remedied by applying one of the commonly used liming materials.

*Soil reaction.* All substances in the presence of water are either acid, alkaline or neutral. The term *reaction* describes the degree or condition of acidity, alkalinity or neutrality. Acidity and alkalinity are expressed by a pH scale on which pH 7 is neutral, numbers below 7 indicate acidity and those above 7 alkalinity. Most cultivated soils have a pH range between 4·5 and 8·0 and may be grouped as follows:

| pH | Reaction |
|---|---|
| Over   7 | Alkaline |
| 7 | Neutral |
| 6·0–6·9 | Slightly acid |
| 5·2–5·9 | Moderately acid |
| Below 5·2 | Very acid |

*Lime requirement.* This is the amount of lime required to raise the pH to approximately 6·5 in the top layer of soil 150 mm (6 in.). This amount varies considerably with the degree of acidity or "sourness", and the type of soil. Heavy (clay) soils and soils rich in organic matter require more lime to raise the pH than other types of soil. For example, to raise the pH from 5·5 to 6·5 on a sandy loam may require about 5 t/ha (2 tons/acre) of ground limestone, but on a clay soil 10–12·5 t/ha (4–5 tons/acre) of ground limestone may be required. The actual lime requirement can be calculated from chemical tests in the laboratory. It is unnecessary to lime soils which have a pH of more than 6·5.

*Indications of soil acidity* (i.e. a need for liming)

(a) Crops failing in patches—particularly the acid-sensitive ones such as *barley* and *sugar-beet*. The plants usually die off or are very unthrifty in the seedling stage.

(b) On grassland, there are poor types of grasses present such as *bents*. Often a *mat* of undecayed vegetation builds up because the acidity reduces the activities of earthworms and bacteria which break down such material.

(c) On arable land, weeds such as *sheep's sorrel, corn marigold* and *spurrey* are common.

(d) *Soil analysis.* Chemical and electrical methods may be used to determine the pH and lime requirements of a soil. Portable testing equipment, using colour charts, are sometimes used to test for pH.

The main benefits of applying lime are:

(1) It neutralizes the acidity or sourness.
(2) It supplies calcium (and sometimes magnesium) for plant nutrition.
(3) It improves soil structure. In well limed soils, plants usually produce more roots and grow better; bacteria are more active in breaking down organic matter. This usually results in a better soil structure and the soil can be cultivated more easily (see also "Soil Structure").
(4) It affects the availability of plant nutrients. The main plant nutrients such as nitrogen, phosphates and potash are freely available on properly limed soils. Too much lime in the soil is likely to make some minor nutrients unavailable to plants, e.g. *manganese, boron, copper* and *zinc*—this is least likely to happen in clay soils.

*pH and crop growth.* To give crops the best opportunity to grow well the soil pH should be near or above the following.

|  | pH |
|---|---|
| Barley, sugar-beet and lucerne | 6·5 |
| Red clover, maize, oil-seed rape | 6·0 |
| Wheat, beans, peas, turnips and swedes | 5·5 |
| Oats, potatoes | 5·0 |
| Rye and lupins | 4·5 |

Lime is removed from the soil by:

(1) *Drainage.* Lime is fairly easily removed in drainage water. 125–2000 kg/ha (1–15 cwt/acre) of calcium carbonate may be

lost annually. The rate of loss is greatest in industrial, smoke polluted areas, areas of high rainfall, well drained soils and soils rich in lime.

(2) *Fertilizers and manures.* Every 1 kg of sulphate of ammonia removes about 1 kg of calcium carbonate from the soil. Poultry manure may also remove some lime.

(3) *Crops.* The approximate amounts of calcium carbonate removed by crops are:

| | |
|---|---|
| Cereals | 1–3 kg (2–6 lb) per tonne (ton) of grain. |
| | 5–7 kg (12–15 lb) per tonne (ton) of straw. |
| Potatoes | 7 kg (15 lb) per 10 tonne (tons) of tubers. |
| Sugar-beet | 23 kg (50 lb) per 15 tonne (tons) of roots. |
| | 90 kg (200 lb) per 13 tonne (tons) of tops. |
| Swedes | 40 kg (90 lb) per 25 tonne (tons) of crop. |
| Kale (carted off) | 180 kg (400 lb) per 22 tonne (tons) of crop. |
| Lucerne hay | 230 kg (500 lb) per 4 tonne (tons) of hay. |

(4) Stock also remove lime, for example, a 500 kg (10 cwt) bullock sold off the farm removes about 16 kg (35 lb) of calcium carbonate in its bones. A 40 kg (90 lb) lamb about 1·3 kg (3 lb) of calcium carbonate and 1000 gal of milk about 16 kg (35 lb) of calcium carbonate.

*Materials commonly used for liming soils*

*Ground limestone or chalk* (also called carbonate of lime and calcium carbonate, $CaCO_3$).

This is obtained by quarrying the limestone or chalk rock and grinding it to a fine powder. It is the commonest liming material used at present.

*Burnt lime* (also called quicklime, lump lime, shell lime and calcium oxide, CaO). This is produced by burning lumps of limestone or chalk rock with coke or other fuel in a kiln. Carbon dioxide is given off and the lumps of burnt lime which are left are sold as lumps, or are ground up ready for mechanical spreading. This "concentrated" form of lime is especially useful for application to remote areas where transport costs are high. Burnt lime may scorch growing crops because it readily takes water from the leaves. When lumps of burnt lime are wetted they break down to a fine powder called *hydrated* or *slaked lime* [Ca(OH)$_2$].

*Hydrated lime* is a good liming material but is usually too expensive for liming the soil.

*Waste limes.* These are liming materials which can sometimes be obtained from industrial processes where lime is used as a purifying material. These limes are cheap but usually contain a lot of water. Some of the sources are: sugar-beet factories, waste from manufacture of sulphate of ammonia, soap works, bleaching, tanneries, etc. Care is needed when using these materials because some may contain harmful substances. Sugar-beet waste lime is also a valuable source of plant nutrients.

A comparison of the various liming materials is as follows:

1 tonne (ton) of burnt lime (CaO) is equivalent to
$$1\cdot37 \text{ tonne (27 cwt) hydrated lime Ca (OH)}_2$$
or $1\cdot83$ tonne (36 cwt) ground limestone CaCO$_3$
or at least $2\cdot5$ tonne (50 cwt) waste lime (usually CaCO$_3$)

The supplier of lime must give a statement of the *neutralizing value* (N.V.) of the liming material—this is really the same as the calcium oxide equivalent.

*Magnesian or dolomitic limestone.* This limestone consists of magnesium carbonate (MgCO$_3$) and CaCO$_3$ and is commonly used as a liming material in areas where it is found. Magnesium carbonate has a better neutralizing value (about one-fifth better) than calcium carbonate. In addition, the magnesium may prevent magnesium deficiency diseases in crops (e.g. interveinal yellowing of leaves in potatoes, sugar-beet, oats) and stock (e.g. "grass-staggers" in grazing animals).

*Cost.* The cost of liming is largely dependent on the transport costs from the lime works to the farm. By dividing the cost per ton of the liming material by the figure for the neutralizing value, the *unit cost* is obtained. In this way it is possible to compare the costs of various liming materials. About half of the cost of liming is paid by government subsidy.

Most farmers now use ground limestone or chalk and arrange for it to be spread mechanically by the suppliers. Where large amounts are required (over 7 t/ha (3 tons/acre)) it is sometimes best to apply it in two dressings, e.g. half before ploughing and half after ploughing.

*Rates of application.* 2·5–25 tonne/hectare (1–10 tons/acre) of calcium carbonate ($CaCO_3$) or its equivalent may be needed to satisfy the lime requirements of a soil. Afterwards, about 2·5–4 t/ha (1–1½ tons/acre) $CaCO_3$ every 4 years should be enough to replace average losses.

## 2. DRAINAGE (SEE ALSO "WATER IN THE SOIL")

Normally, the soil can only hold some of the rainwater which falls on it. The remainder either runs off or is evaporated from the surface or soaks through the soil to the subsoil. If surplus water is prevented from moving through the soil and subsoil it soon fills up all the pore-spaces and this will kill or stunt the crops growing there.

The *water-table* is the level in the soil or subsoil below which all the pore space is filled with water. This is not easy to see or measure in clay soils but can be seen in open textured soils (see Fig. 27). The water-table level fluctuates through the year and in the British Isles is usually highest in February and lowest in September; the greater

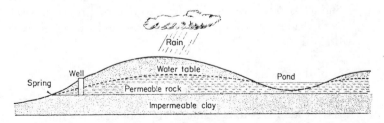

FIG. 27. Diagram showing position of a water-table and its effect on the water levels in the well and pond.

amount of evaporation, much more transpiration and lower rain-fall (usually) in summer allow the level to fall in late summer and early autumn. This is shown by the water level falling in ponds and shallow wells, some springs drying up and wet parts of fields drying out.

In chalk and limestone areas, and in most sandy and gravelly soils, water can drain away easily into the porous subsoil. These are *free-draining* soils. Steep slopes also drain freely.

On most other types of farmland some sort of artificial *field drainage* is necessary to carry away the surplus water and so keep the water-table at a reasonable level. For most arable farm crops the water-table should be about 600 mm (2 ft) or more below the surface; for grass land 300–450 mm (1–1½ ft) is sufficient.

Some of the signs of bad drainage are:

(a) Machinery is easily "bogged down" in wet weather.
(b) Stock grazing pastures in wet weather easily damage and trample holes in the sward (poaching).
(c) Water lies about in pools on the surface for many days after heavy rain.
(d) Weeds such as rushes, sedges, horsetail, tussock grass and meadowsweet are common in grassland. Peat forms in places which have been very wet for a long time.
(e) Young plants are pale green or yellow in colour and unthrifty, when compared with the greener and more vigorous plants on drier land nearby.
(f) Subsoil is often various shades of blue, or grey compared with shades of reddish brown, yellow and orange in well drained soil.

Some of the practical advantages of good drainage are:

(a) Well drained land is better aerated and the crops grow better and are less likely to be damaged by root-decaying fungi.
(b) The soil dries out better in spring and so warms up quicker and can be worked early.

(c) Plants are encouraged to form a deeper and more extensive root system. In this way they can often obtain more plant food.

(d) Grassland is firmer—especially after wet periods. Good drainage is essential for high density stocking and where cattle are out-wintered if serious poaching of the pastures is to be avoided. Rushes and other moisture-loving weeds usually disappear after draining wet land.

(e) Disease risk from parasites is reduced. A good example is the liver fluke—this must pass part of its life cycle in a water snail found on badly drained land.

(f) Inter-row cultivations and harvesting of root crops and potatoes can be carried out more efficiently.

(g) Fertilizers and manures will give better results because the crop can grow more vigorously.

(h) Crops grown under contract, e.g. vining peas, can usually be planted and harvested at the proper time on well-drained land.

The main methods used to remove surplus water and control the water-table are:

(a) Open channels or ditches.
(b) Underground pipe drains—tiles and plastic.
(c) Mole drains.

*Ditches and open drains.* Ditches may be adequate to drain an area by themselves but they usually serve as outlets for undergound drains. They are capable of dealing with large volumes of water in very wet periods. The size of a ditch varies according to the area it serves (see Fig. 28). Ditches should be kept cleaned out to their original depth as often as necessary—usually annually or biennially. The spoil removed should be spread well clear of the edge of the ditch. Many different types of machines are now available for making new ditches and cleaning neglected ones.

Small open channels 10–60 metres (yards) apart are used for draining hill grazing areas. These are either dug by hand using a special spade or made with a special type of plough, drawn by a crawler

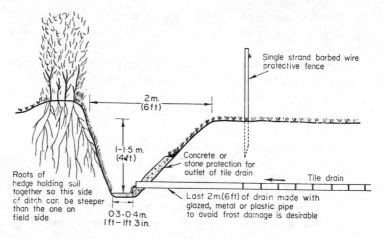

Single strand barbed wire
protective fence

2 m.
(6 ft)

1-1·5 m.
(4 ft)

Concrete or
stone protection for
outlet of tile drain

Tile drain

Roots of
hedge holding soil
together so this side
of ditch can be steeper
than the one on
field side

0·3-0·4 m.
1 ft - 1 ft 3 in.

Last 2 m.(6 ft) of drain made with
glazed, metal or plastic pipe
to avoid frost damage is desirable

FIG. 28. Section through a typical field ditch and tile drain.

tractor. Similar open channels are used on low lying meadow land
where underground drainage is not possible.

*Underground drains—general.* The distance between drains which
is necessary for good drainage depends on the soil texture. In clay
soils the small pore spaces restrict the movement of water and so
the drains must be spaced much closer together than on the lighter

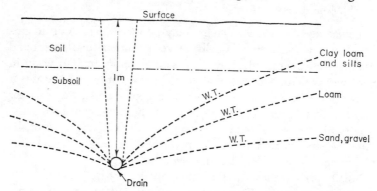

Surface

Soil

Clay loam
and silts

Subsoil    1 m

W.T.                    Loam

W.T.

W.T.                Sand, gravel

Drain

FIG. 29. Diagram to show how the steepness of the water-table
(W.T.) varies with different types of soil.

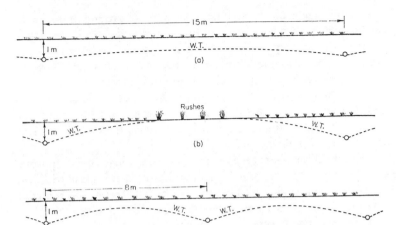

FIG. 30. Diagram showing the effect of spacing of drains on the water table (W.T.) (a) sandy loam, (b) and (c) silt or clay loam.

types of soil where water can flow freely through the large pore spaces (see Figs. 29 and 30).

*Underground drains—pipe drains (tiles or plastic).* The correct spacing of underground drains depends on the permeability of the soil and subsoil. The small pore spaces in fine textured soils restrict the movement of water and so the drains must be placed closer together than in coarse textured and creviced soils where water can flow more freely. The approximate spacings in various soils is set out below.

| Soil type | Depth of drains | | Distance between pipe drains | |
|---|---|---|---|---|
| | m | ft | (metres or yards) | chains |
| Sand, gravel | 0·90–1·20 | 3–4 | 40–100 | 2–5 |
| Fine sand | 0·75–0·90 | 2½–3 | 20–50 | 1–2·5 |
| Loams | 0·75–0·90 | 2½–3 | 10–35 | 0·5–1·7 |
| Peats | 1·00–1·50 | 3½–5 | 7–50 | 0·7–2·5 |
| Silts and clays | 0·60–0·75 | 2 –2½ | 7–20 | 0·7–1·0 |
| Clays (with mole drains) | 0·60–0·75 | 2 –2½ | 50–150 | 2·5–7·5 |

Tile drainage is the commonest type of underground drainage. It can be used on all types of soil but on clay soils it is usually restricted to main drains only because of the high cost. Tiles are made of burnt clay, but sometimes pipes made of concrete are used. They are usually 300 mm (1 ft) long and of various diameters. 75 mm (3 in.) diameter tiles are used for the ordinary side or lateral drains: 100, 150 and 220 mm (4, 6 and 9 in.) diameter tiles are used for the main drains. The size of tile required will depend on the rainfall, area to for be drained, fall, and soil structure.

When tile drainage is used on clays and heavy loam soils, a porous material such as gravel or clinker should be used as backfill to allow the water to move down to the tiles easily. The cost of this material is reduced when narrow trenches are dug for the tiles.

There are many types of trenching and tile laying machines available. Most tile drainage work is done by specialist contractors.

Various types of *plastic* and *polythene* pipes are now being used instead of tiles for underground drains. They are supplied in 10-chain lengths and are laid in the soil by special machines—some of which are modified mole-ploughs. 50 mm (2 in.) diameter pipes are used for the side drains and 100 mm (4 in.) diameter pipes are used for the main drains.

The drainage water enters through holes or slits in the walls of the pipes which may be smooth or corrugated.

Some of the machines which lay the plastic pipes can also lay porous filling above the pipes. Most plastic pipe drains are laid by contractors. Although plastic pipes cost more than tiles the overall cost of pipes plus laying is less for the plastic system.

*Underground drains—mole drainage.* This is a cheap drainage method which can be used in some fields. Although the method is sometimes used on peat soils it is normally used in fields which have:

(a) *clay subsoil* (no stones, sand or gravel patches),
(b) *suitable fall* 50–350 mm (2–14 in.)/chain,
(c) *reasonably smooth surface.*

A mole plough, which has a torpedo or bullet shaped "mole"

attached to a steel coulter or blade, forms a cylindrical channel in
the subsoil. The three main types are:

(1) mounted on three-point linkage,
(2) on wheeled carrying frame and adjustable for depth by winch,
(3) simple skid type (see Fig. 31).

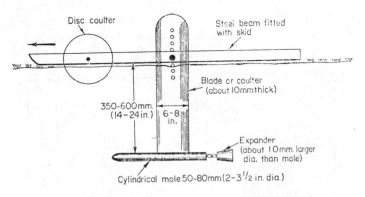

Disc coulter

Steel beam fitted
with skid

Blade or coulter
(about 10mm thick)

350–600mm.
(14–24 in.)   6–8
in.

Expander
(about 10mm larger
dia. than mole)

Cylindrical mole 50–80mm (2–3½ in. dia.)

FIG. 31. Diagram of a simple (skid) type of mole plough.

The best conditions for mole draining are when the subsoil is
damp enough to be plastic and forms a good surface on the mole
channel, and also sufficiently dry to form cracks as the mole plough
passes (see Fig. 32). If the surface is dry the tractor hauling the

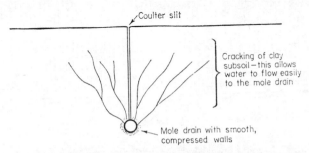

Coulter slit

Cracking of clay
subsoil—this allows
water to flow easily
to the mole drain

Mole drain with smooth,
compressed walls

FIG. 32. Section through a mole drain and surrounding soil.

plough can get a better grip. The plough should be drawn slowly about 3 km.p.h. (2 m.p.h.) otherwise the vacuum created is likely to spoil the mole. Reasonably dry weather after moling will allow the surface of the mole to harden and so it should last longer.

Mole drains are drawn 3–4 metres (yds) apart except on "ridge and furrow" land where one or more drains are drawn along the furrows. For best results the moles should be drawn through the porous back filling of a tiled or plastic main drain (see Figs. 33 and 34). 1½–2 chains of tiled main are usually required per acre (4–5

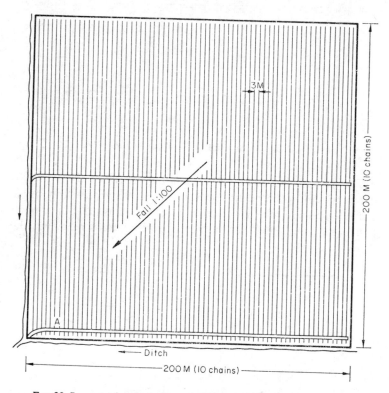

FIG. 33. Layout of mole drainage (with tiled main) in a six-acre field. Section through drains A shown in Fig. 34.

chains/ha). The mains are semi-permanent and a new set of mole drains can be drawn every 5–15 years as required. A large wheeled tractor can pull a 50 mm (2 in.) mole 350–450 mm (14–18 in.) deep. For larger and deeper drains a crawler tractor is required.

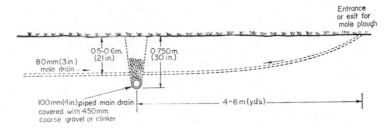

Fig. 34. Section through tile drain shown in Fig. 33 to show how water from the mole drain can enter the pipe drain through the porous backfilling.
(See also M.A.F.F. Field Drainage leaflets Nos. 1–13.)

## 3. IRRIGATION (SEE ALSO "WATER IN THE SOIL")

Irrigation can be used to supply water to crops which are suffering from drought. If water is not applied at such times then the crops are checked and may die. This means low yields and the quality may be poor.

At present, in this country, it is usual to measure irrigation water, like rainfall, in inches, e.g. 1 in. per acre = 22,620 gallons or 101 tons
= 254 m³/ha.

To grow satisfactorily, most crops in the British Isles will require the following amounts of water if their leaves are covering the ground:

25 mm (1 in.) every 14–16 days in April and September,
25 mm (1 in.) every 10–12 days in May and August,
25 mm (1 in.) every 7– 8 days in June and July.

For best results, this must be evenly spread over the growing season—especially on the lighter types of soil. Clay and silt and soils rich in organic matter can hold more reserves of water and so are not so dependent on even distribution. The approximate amounts of available water which various soils can hold are shown in Table 3A.

TABLE 3A

| Soil type | Approximate amounts of *available* water per unit depth of soil | |
| --- | --- | --- |
| | mm/cm | in./ft |
| Sandy | 0·4–0·8 | ½–1 |
| Sandy loam | 0·8–1·6 | 1–2 |
| Clay | 1·6–2·0 | 2–2½ |
| Loams and silts | 2·0–2·5 | 2½–3 |
| Black Fen (organic) | 2·5–3·3 | 3–4 |

The amount of organic matter in the soil can alter the water holding capacity very considerably, e.g. it is increased by the organic matter produced by leys and by the application of F.Y.M. Soil which is consolidated holds more water per unit depth than loosely packed soil.

The water capacity of the soil and sub-soil are usually different depending on texture differences, degree of consolidation and organic matter content.

The amount of water available to a crop at any one time depends on the capacity of the soil per unit depth, and the depth of soil from

TABLE 3B

| Crop | Rooting depth | |
| --- | --- | --- |
| | mm | in. |
| Potatoes, cereals, pastures | 350–450 | 14–18 |
| Beans, peas, conserved grass | 450–600 | 18–24 |
| Sugar-beet | 600–750 | 24–30 |
| Lucerne | over 1200 | over 48 |

which the roots can take up water. The figures in Table 3B are average rooting depths; these would be greater on deep, well-drained soils and less on shallow, badly-drained or panned soils.

From the above tables (3A and 3B) it can be calculated that a crop of peas, for example, growing on a silty loam soil would have about 100–150 mm (4–6 in.) of water available to it when the soil is at field capacity and this should be sufficient to keep it growing satisfactorily for a few weeks if no rain falls. If irrigation is possible, it is advisable not to let the amount of available water, within root range, fall below 50% of the maximum field capacity. This could be calculated from average transpiration rates of 2·5–4 mm (0·1 in.) per day or would be indicated by finding that it is difficult to form the soil into a ball which will hold together (this test does not apply to sandy soils).

The greatest need for irrigation in the British Isles is in the south-east, where the lower rainfall and higher potential evaporation and transpiration means that irrigation would be beneficial about 9 years out of 10. In the wetter western and northern areas the need is much less. Potatoes and intensively managed grassland usually produce the best profits from irrigation.

In many parts of this country very limited amounts of water are available for irrigation although much could be done to improve this situation by the construction of reservoirs to conserve the winter surplus. Grants are available for permanent works of this kind (see *MAFF Bulletin* No. 202—*Water for Irrigation*).

More experimental work is required to determine the stages of growth at which crops are most responsive to irrigation and also minimum water requirements, for example:

It is known that peas are most responsive at "start of flowering" and "pod swelling" stages.

Also, if a maincrop potato variety which normally produces a lot of tubers (e.g. King Edward) is irrigated before the tubers are marble size too many small tubers and a low ware yield may result. Excessive amounts of water are likely to produce poor quality tubers.

Irrigation of sugar-beet before the leaves meet across the rows encourages surface root development instead of deep rooting which would be less dependent on irrigation.

Table 4 is a guide to the rate at which various soil types can absorb water and so the rate at which irrigation water should be applied when using ordinary sprinklers and rain-guns. These rates could be considerably increased if very fine droplets were used but this is considered to be uneconomical at present. When irrigation water, or rain, falls on a dry soil it saturates the top layers of soil to full field capacity before moving further down—unless the soil is deeply cracked (e.g. clay) and some of the water will run down the cracks.

TABLE 4

| Soil type | Time (hr) required to absorb 25mm (1 in.) of water | Depth of soil (at wilting point) which is wetted by 25 mm (1 in.) of water | |
|-----------|----------------------|------------------|------------|
| Sandy | 1–2 | 300–600 mm | (12–24 in.) |
| Loams | 3 | 100–150 mm | (4–6 in.) |
| Clay | 4–5 | 120–150 mm | (5–6 in.) |

Irrigation water is applied by:

(a) *Rotary sprinklers.* This is the commonest method used. Each rotating sprinkler covers an area about 21–36 metres (70–120 ft) in diameter; the sprinklers are usually spaced at 10·5 m (35 ft) apart along the supply line and the line is moved about 18 m (60 ft) for each setting. 50 such sprinklers would cover one hectare (2½ acres) and each sprinkler applies about 18–45 litres (4–10 gallons) per minute. Special nozzles can be used to apply a fine spray 2·5 mm (0·1 in.) per hour for frost protection of fruit crops and potatoes; icicles form on the plants but the latent heat of freezing protects the plant tissue from damage.

(b) *Rain guns.* These are used on grassland and crops such as sugar-beet which are covering the ground. The droplets are large. Diameter of area covered may be 60–120 m. Some types are used for organic irrigation (slurry).

(c) *Spraylines.* These apply the water gently and are used mainly for horticultural crops.

(d) *Surface channels.* This method requires almost level or contoured land. It is wasteful of land, water and labour.

(e) *Underground pipes.* On level land, water can be dammed in the ditches and allowed to flow up the drainage pipes into the subsoil and lower soil layers. This is drainage in reverse!

(f) Large units are now available which cover several acres at one setting; they may be mounted on a tractor or wheeled carriage and supply water through sprinklers and/or rain guns.

(See also *M.A.F. Bulletin* No. 138—*Irrigation*, and STL. leaflet No. 71.)

## 4. WARPING

This is a process of soil formation where land, lying between high and low water levels, alongside a tidal river, is deliberately flooded with muddy water. The area to be treated is surrounded by earth banks fitted with sluice gates. At high tide, water is allowed to flood quickly onto the enclosed area and is run off slowly through sluice gates at low tide. The fineness of the material deposited will depend on the length of time allowed for settling—the coarse particles will settle very quickly but the finer particles may take one or more days to settle. The depth of the deposit may be 18 in. in one winter. When enough alluvium is deposited it is then drained and prepared for cropping. Sections dug through the subsoil clearly show separate deposition layers.

These soils are very fertile and are usually intensively cropped with arable crops such as *potatoes*, *sugar-beet*, *peas*, *wheat* and *barley*.

Part of the land around the Humber estuary is warpland, and the best is probably that in the lower Trent valley. Most of this work was done last century.

## 5. CLAYING

The texture of "blow-away " sandy soils and black fen soils can be improved by applying 250–750 t/ha (100–300 tons/acre) of clay or marl (a lime-rich clay). If the subsoil of the area is clay this can be dug out of trenches and roughly scattered by a dragline excavator. In other cases the clay is dug in pits and transported in special lorry spreaders. Rotary cultivators help to spread the clay. If the work is done in late summer or autumn, the winter frosts help to break down the lumps of clay. (See M.A.F.F. leaflet, No. 18.)

### Tillage and Cultivations

Cultivations are field operations which attempt to alter the soil structure. The main object is to provide a suitable seed-bed in which a crop can be planted and will grow satisfactorily; sometimes cultivations are used to kill weeds, or bury the remains of previous crops. The timing of cultivations—particularly with regard to the weather and on the heavier soils—is more an art than a science and is largely based on experience. The cost of the work can be considerably reduced by good timing and use of the right implements. Ideally, a good seed-bed should be prepared with the minimum amount of working and the least loss of moisture. On heavy soil and in a wet season, some loss of moisture is sometimes desirable. On the medium and heavy soils full advantage should be taken of weathering effects; for example, ploughing in the autumn will allow frost to break the soil into a crumb structure; wetting and drying alternately will have a similar effect.

SEED–BED REQUIREMENTS FOR VARIOUS CROPS

(1) *Cereals.* (a) *Autumn planted.* The object here is to provide a tilth (seed-bed condition) which consists of fine material and lumps about fist-size. It should allow for the seed to be drilled and easily covered and the surface should remain rough after planting. The lumps on the surface will prevent the heavier soils from "capping"

easily in a mild wet winter and they also protect the base of the cereals from the harmful effects of very cold winds. Harrowing and/or rolling may be done in the spring to break up a soil cap which may have formed and to firm the soil around plants which have been heaved by frost action.

(b) *Spring planted*. A fairly fine seed-bed is required in the spring-time (very fine if grasses and clovers are to be undersown). If the seed-bed is dry or very loose after drilling it should be consolidated by rolling—this is especially important if the crop is undersown and where the soil is stony.

(2) *Root crops*, e.g. sugar-beet, swedes, and carrots: also *kale*. These crops have small seeds and so the seed-bed must be as fine as possible, level, and firm. This is particularly important when precision drills and very low seed rates (to reduce seed and thinning costs) are used. Good, early, ploughing with uniform, well packed and broken furrow slices will considerably reduce the amount of work required in the spring. If possible, deep cultivations should be avoided in the springtime so keeping frost mould on top and leaving unweathered soil well below the surface. Roots are usually sown on ridges in the higher rainfall areas; this avoids damage by surface water and also makes singling and harvesting easier.

(3) *Direct seeding of grasses and clovers*. Same as for roots.

(4) *Beans and peas*. Similar to cereals—but tilth need not be so fine. Peas grown on light soils may be drilled into the ploughed surface (or after one stroke of the harrow) if the ploughing has been well done.

(5) *Potatoes*. This crop is usually planted in ridges 600–750 mm (2–2½ ft) wide and so deep cultivations are necessary. The fineness of tilth required depends on how the crop will be managed after planting. A fairly rough, damp seed-bed is usually preferable to a fine, dry tilth which has been worked too much. Some crops are worked many times after planting—such as harrowing down the ridges, ridging-up again, deep cultivations between the ridges and final earthing-up. The main object of these cultivations is to control weeds but the implements often damage the roots of the potato plants.

Most annual weeds can be controlled by spraying the ridges when the potato sprouts start to appear. This can replace most of the inter-row cultivations and reduce the number of clods produced by the rubber-tyred tractor wheels.

RECENT DEVELOPMENTS

*Direct Drilling* (slit-seeding, zero tillage) and *Minimal Cultivations* techniques are now becoming widely established alternatives to conventional cultivations on many farms and on a wide range of soil types including difficult clays.

For *direct drilling*, several types of special drills are available, using such developments as heavily weighted discs for cutting slits, strong cultivator tines, or modified rotary cultivators.

The *advantages* of the technique are:

(1) Considerable saving in time (less than half the normal).
(2) It may be possible when normal cultivations are not, but this is not to be encouraged—particularly on heavy soils.
(3) Very little loss of soil moisture when compared with ordinary cultivations.
(4) It has a controlling effect on "take-all" in cereal crops and usually gives higher yields of plumper grains.
(5) Better control of wild oats and blackgrass because shed seeds left on the surface are eaten or otherwise destroyed and dormancy is not encouraged by burial of the seeds.
(6) Better soil structure—which also means better drainage: this is especially so when the technique is introduced at a time when the soil has a good structure. Normal cultivations can destroy a good structure built up by a period in grass. When the technique is used for several years, organic matter residues accumulate in the surface layer of the soil where it is of greatest benefit and is not diluted by burial (e.g. ploughing) and mixing with deeper soil layers.

Some *disadvantages* are:

(1) Does not bury trash, so burning of stubble or destruction of grass swards with chemicals is necessary.
(2) Should not be used where perennial weeds such as couch, field

bindweed, coltsfoot, and corn mint are abundant. However, a
new herbicide—glyphosate—may be used to destroy these.

(3) Winter wheat crops take longer to establish in the firm soil, so
should be sown before the end of October. Also, more likely
to get trouble with hares and rabbits on the firmer soil and
especially if stubble is left.

(4) Is not a success if soils are badly drained.

(5) If stubble is badly rutted after harvest, this must be remedied
by conventional cultivations.

(6) Slug damage can be serious—especially in wet conditions—
and slug pellets should be used to control them (these may be
placed in the slits with the seed).

(7) Heavy soils may crack along the slits in very dry weather and
the seed may not establish properly.

Possible uses for the technique are:

(a) For cereals in a continuous cereal system or following peas,
beans, oil-seed rape, potatoes. If following grass (destroyed by
chemicals), trouble may arise from grass seedlings growing in
the cereals—especially if sown in autumn.

(b) Kale after grass; establishes well, even in dry weather, and the
undisturbed turf is much firmer for grazing in autumn.

(c) Root crops, such as sugar beet, on light soils.

(d) Oil-seed rape after cereals or other crops.

(e) Green forage crops after early-harvested cereals for autumn
and early winter grazing.

*Minimal cultivations* systems are those using various types of
cultivators, instead of ploughing, and in such a way that only the
minimum depth of soil is moved to allow drilling to take place.

TILLAGE IMPLEMENTS

The main implements used for tillage are:

*Ploughs.* Ploughing is the first operation in seed-bed preparation
on most farms and is likely to remain so for some time yet, although
many farmers are now using rotary cultivators, heavy cultivators
with fixed or spring tines, and mechanically driven digging or
pulverizing machines, as alternatives to the plough. Good ploughing

is probably the best method of burying weeds and the remains of previous crops; it can also set up the soil so that good frost penetration is possible. Fast ploughing produces a more broken furrow slice than slow steady work. The *mounted* or *semi-mounted plough* is replacing the *trailed type* on most farms because of ease of handling. *General purpose mouldboards* are commonly used; the shorter *digger* types (concave mouldboards) break the furrow slices better and are often used on the lighter soils. *Deep digger ploughs* are used where deep ploughing is required, e.g. for roots or potatoes. The *one-way* (*reversible*) type of plough is fairly popular for crops such as roots and peas: it has right-hand and left-hand mouldboards and no openings or finishes have to be made when ploughing so the seedbed can be kept level. *Round-and-round* ploughing with the ordinary plough has almost the same effect although this is not a suitable method on all fields.

The proper use of skim and disc coulters and careful setting of the plough for depth, width and pitch can greatly improve the quality of the ploughing. The furrow slice can only be turned over satisfactorily if the depth is less than about two-thirds the width; the usual widths of ordinary plough bodies vary from 200–350 mm (8–14 in.). If possible, it is desirable to vary the depth of ploughing from year to year to avoid the formation of a plough pan. Very deep ploughing which brings up several inches of poorly weathered subsoil must be undertaken with care: the long-term effects will probably be worthwhile but, for a few years afterwards, the soil may be rather sticky and difficult to work. Buried weed seeds, such as wild oats which have fallen down cracks, may be brought to the surface and may spoil the following crops. "*Chisel ploughing*" is a modern term used to describe the work done by a heavy duty cultivator with special spring or fixed tines—it does not move or invert all the soil as the ordinary plough does. *Disc* ploughs have large saucer-shaped discs instead of shares and mouldboards. Compared with the ordinary mouldboard ploughs they do not cut all the ground or invert the soil so well but they can work in harder and stickier soil conditions. They are more popular in dry countries. Double mouldboard *ridging* ploughs are used for potatoes and some root crops in the wetter areas.

*Cultivators.* These are tined implements which are used to break up the soil clods (to ploughing depth). Some have tines which are rigid or are held by very strong springs which only give when an obstruction such as a strong tree root is struck. Others have spring tines which are constantly moving according to the resistance of the soil—they have a very good pulverizing effect and can often be pulled at a high speed; they can be useful for dragging the rhizomes of weeds, such as couch, to the surface. The shares on the tines may be of various widths. The pitch of the tines draws the implement into the soil. Depth can be controlled by tractor linkage or wheels. The timing of cultivations is very important if the operation is to be effective.

*Harrows.* There are many types of harrows: the zigzag type, which has staggered tines, is the commonest. Harrow tines are usually straight, but may vary in length and strength on the heavy and light types. *Drag harrows* have curved ends on the tines.

These implements are often used to complete the work of the cultivator. Besides breaking the soil down to a fine tilth they can have a useful consolidating effect due to shaking the soil about.

*"Dutch"* harrows have spikes fitted in a heavy wooden frame and are useful for levelling a seed-bed as well as breaking clods.

Some harrows, e.g. the chain type, consist of flexible links joined together to form a rectangle. These follow an uneven surface better, and do not jump about so much on grassland as the zigzag type. Most chain harrows have spikes fitted on one side. They are sometimes used to roll-up weeds such as "couch" grass.

Special types of harrows fitted with knife-like tines are used for improving matted grassland, by tearing out surface trash.

*Power-driven* (reciprocating) harrows, on which rows of tines are made to move at right angles to the direction of travel, can result in much better movement of the soil at one pass. They are proving useful on farms where modern methods of preparing seedbeds for sugar beet and potatoes are used.

*Hoes.* These are implements used for controlling weeds between the rows in root crops. Various shaped blades, and discs may be fitted to them. Most types are either front, mid or rear mounted on a tractor. The front and mid mounted types are controlled by the steering of the tractor driver. The rear mounted types usually require a second person for steering the hoe.

*Disc harrows* consist of "gangs" of saucer-shaped discs about 300–600 mm (12–24 in.) in diameter. They have a cutting and consolidating effect on the soil and this is particularly useful when working a seed-bed on ploughed-out grassland.

The more the discs are *angled*, the greater will be:

(a) the depth of penetration,
(b) the cutting and breaking effect on the clods,
(c) the draught.

To increase the effect of the operation, the rear gangs should be angled more than the front gangs. Disc harrows are widely used for preparing all kinds of seed-beds but it should be remembered that they are expensive implements to use. They have a heavy draught and lots of wearing parts (discs, bearings and linkages) so should only be used when harrows would not be suitable. They tend to cut the rhizomes of weeds such as "couch" and creeping thistle into short pieces which are easily carried about and so encourages the spread of these weeds. Discing of old grassland before ploughing will usually allow the plough to do better work and a better seed-bed can be made. Heavy discs, and especially those with scalloped edges, are very useful for working in chopped straw after combining.

*Rotary cultivators* (*e.g. rotavator*). This type of implement consists of curved blades which rotate round a horizontal shaft set at right angles to the direction of travel. The shaft is driven from the P.T.O. of the tractor; depth is controlled by a land wheel or skid. This implement can produce a good tilth in difficult conditions and in many cases may replace all other implements in seed-bed preparation. A light fluffy tilth is sometimes produced which may "cap" easily if wet weather follows. The fineness of tilth can be controlled by the forward speed of the tractor—fast speed, coarse tilth. It is a very useful implement for mixing into the soil the remains of kale and sprout crops, or straw. The rotating action of the blades helps to drive the implement forward; so extra care must be taken when going down steep slopes. The blades cut up rhizomatous weeds (e.g. couch) but if the implement is used several times (at 10–14 day intervals) in growing weather it can completely destroy the couch either by burying the sprouted pieces or throwing them out on the surface to die off in drying winds. A similar method (working 200–250 mm (8–10 in.) deep) will control bracken.

In wet heavy soils the rotating action of the blades may have a smearing effect on the soil. This can usually be avoided by having the blades properly angled. "Rotavating" of ploughed or cultivated land when the surface is frozen in winter can produce a good seed-bed for cereals in the spring without any further working or loss of moisture; if there is couch present and the weather is dry, much of it may die off. Narrow rotary cultivator units are available for working between rows of root crops.

A recently introduced high-speed rotary cultivator is useful for quick shallow working either for stubble cleaning or seed-bed preparation.

*Rolls.* These are used to consolidate the top few inches of the soil so that plant roots can keep in contact with the soil particles and the soil can hold more moisture. They are also used for crushing clods and breaking surface crusts (caps). Rolls should not be used when the soil is wet—this is especially important on the heavier soils. The two main types of rolls are the *flat* roll which has a smooth surface and the *Cambridge* or *ring* roll which has a ribbed surface and consists of a number of heavy iron wheels or rings (about 70 mm wide) each of which has a ridge about 40 mm high. The rings are free to move independently and this helps to keep the surface clean. The ribbed or corrugated surface left by the Cambridge roll provides an excellent seed-bed on which to sow grass and clover seeds or roots. Also, it is less likely to "cap" than a flat rolled surface.

When rolling a growing crop, e.g. young cereals, tractor wheel-slip must be avoided as this will tear out the seedlings.

Very heavy rolls are sometimes used for levelling fields in the spring prior to taking a white clover seed crop.

*A furrow press* is a special type of very heavy ring roller (usually with three or four wheels) used for compressing the furrow slices after ploughing—it is usually attached to and pulled alongside the plough.

See simplified cultivation, Table 5, p. 87.

## PANS

A *pan* is a hard, cement-like layer in the soil or subsoil which can be very harmful because it prevents surplus water draining away freely and restricts root growth.

Such a layer may be caused by ploughing at the same depth every year. This is a *plough pan* and is partly caused by the base of the plough sliding along the furrow. It is more likely to occur if rubber-tyred tractors are used when the soil is wet and there is some wheel-slip which has a smearing effect on the bottom of the furrow. Plough pans are more likely to form on the heavier types of soil. They can be broken up by using a *subsoiler*—a strong tine which can penetrate deeper than the plough, or, if the pan is not too deep, it can be destroyed by deep ploughing.

Pans may also be formed by the deposition of *iron compounds*, and sometimes *humus*, in layers in the soil or subsoil. These are often called *chemical* or *iron pans* and may be destroyed in the same way as plough pans. *Clay pans* are sometimes formed in certain soil formation processes.

## SOIL CAPPING

A soil *cap* is a hard crust, often only about 25 mm (1 in.) thick, which sometimes forms on the surface of a soil.

It is most likely to form on soils which are low in organic matter. Heavy rain or large droplets of water from rain guns (see "Irrigation") may cause soil capping. Tractor wheels (especially if slipping), trailers and other heavy machinery can also cause capping in wet weather.

Although a soil cap is easily destroyed by weathering (e.g. frost,

TABLE 5. A SIMPLIFIED CULTIVATION TABLE (A ROTARY CULTIVATOR OR OTHER POWER DRIVEN MACHINE MAY BE USED INSTEAD OF SOME OF THE OPERATIONS GIVEN BELOW)

| | | Autumn | Spring |
|---|---|---|---|
| *Winter cereals* | After grass | Plough, disc and/or harrow, drill, harrow. | Harrow and/or roll (if necessary). |
| | After potatoes | Cultivate or disc, drill, harrow. | |
| *Spring cereals* | After grass | Plough. | Harrow and/or disc, drill, harrow, roll. |
| | After cereals | Plough or disc and cultivate several times and leave in ridges over winter. | Harrow and/or disc, drill, harrow, roll. |
| *Roots, e.g.* sugar-beet, swedes | After cereals | Stubble cleaning, plough-in F.Y.M. | Disc and/or harrow, roll, drill; inter-row hoeing. In the wetter areas, the field is ridged up before drilling. |
| *Kale* | After cereals | Stubble cleaning, plough-in F.Y.M. | |
| *Potatoes* | After cereals | Rotavate or disc, plough. | Cross-plough, if necessary. Cultivate (twice), harrow, ridge, plant and split ridges, followed by inter-row cultivations and finally earthing up. |
| *Peas* | After grass | Plough, fast and well. | Cultivation after planting may be replaced by chemical weed control. Harrow, drill. |

or wetting and drying) or by cultivations, it may do harm while it lasts by:

(a) preventing water moving into the soil,
(b) preventing air moving into and out of the soil in wet weather,
(c) hindering the development of seedlings from small seeds such as grasses and clovers, roots and vegetables.

### CONTROL OF WEEDS BY CULTIVATION

The introduction of chemicals which kill weeds has reduced the importance of cultivation as a means of controlling weeds. The cereal crops are now regarded by many farmers as the *cleaning crops* instead of the roots and potato crops, mainly because chemical spraying of weeds in cereals is very effective.

However, weeds should be tackled in every way possible and there are still occasions when it is worthwhile to use cultivation methods.

*Annual weeds* can be tackled by:

(a) Working the stubble after harvest (e.g. discing, cultivating or rotavating) to encourage seeds to germinate: these young weeds can later be destroyed by harrowing or ploughing.
(b) Preparing a "false" seed-bed in spring to allow the weed seeds to germinate—these can be killed by cultivation before sowing root crops.
(c) Inter-row hoeing of root crops which can destroy a lot of annual weeds and some perennials.

*Perennial weeds*, e.g. couch grass, creeping thistle, docks, field bindweed and coltsfoot, can only be satisfactorily controlled by fallowing (i.e. cultivating the soil periodically through the growing season instead of cropping) but this is expensive. A fair amount of control can be obtained by short-term working in dry weather.

Couch grass is easily killed by drying winds if the rhizomes can be dragged out to the surface free of soil. This may be done in August and September, or in the early spring, using cultivators or shallow ploughing to loosen the soil, followed by drag or spring tined harrows to drag it out on top and shake off the soil; dry weather is necessary to do this properly.

In damp soil conditions, the rotary cultivator can be used three or four times at 2–3-week intervals to chop up and exhaust couch grass rhizomes. It is very important that the first time over should be on firm soil (e.g. stubble), and the tractor moving in low gear. Chopping the rhizomes into short pieces encourages nearly all the buds to send out shoots and so helps to exhaust them.

The deeper rooted bindweed, docks, thistles, and coltsfoot cannot be satisfactorily controlled by these methods, but periodic hoeing and cultivating between the rows of root crops can considerably reduce these weeds by cutting off new shoots and so exhausting them.

*Fallowing.* The object of a long-term fallow is to dry out the soil by frequent working and so dry out and kill the perennial weeds. On the medium to lighter soils this is done by frequent cultivations. On heavy soil, the field is ploughed when damp in spring to make it dry into hard lumps. These lumps are then moved by cross-ploughing or deep cultivations to help dry them out. During the summer, alternate periods of wetting and drying break the lumps down to a fine tilth and then annual weeds may germinate to be destroyed by further working. Fallowing is not very common nowadays because of the cost of the work and the loss of profit on a crop.

One of the best methods of controlling wild onion is by taking seven spring-sown crops in succession and ploughing each year in November.

Thorough cultivations which provide the most suitable conditions for rapid healthy growth of the crop may result in the crop outgrowing and smothering the weeds.

### Suggestions for Classwork

*Examine:*

(a) Samples of rock, e.g. granite, basalt, chalk, limestone.
(b) Various soil types in the field or in suitable blocks in the classroom, e.g. clay, sand, loam, peat. Handle them when wet and dry. If possible, examine the soil profiles.
(c) Note the crumbling effect on clods of frost action, and wetting and drying.

(d) Visit farms on clay, loam and sandy soils and discuss the management of these soils.

(e) Visit a drainage scheme in progress. Note how levels are taken and the use of sighting and boning rods.

(f) See seed-beds being prepared for cereals, roots and potatoes and make notes on the cultivation work which was carried out.

# CHAPTER 3

# FERTILIZERS AND MANURES

## Supplying Plant Nutrients to the Soil

If good crops are to be continuously removed from a field or a farm then there must be at least as many nutrients returned to the soil as have been removed in the crops. Table 6 gives average figures for nutrients removed by various crops.

When supplying nutrients to the soil it is usual to apply more than enough for the needs of each crop because some nutrients may be lost by drainage (e.g. nitrogen and potash) and some will become "fixed" or unavailable in the soil (e.g. phosphate). Where one crop, e.g. potatoes or roots, has been heavily manured with fertilizers and F.Y.M., it may be possible to reduce the amount of nutrients supplied to the following crop.

*Nitrogen* is supplied by fertilizers, organic matter (e.g. F.Y.M.), nodule bacteria on legumes (e.g. clovers, peas, beans, lucerne), and nitrogen fixing micro-organisms in the soil. It is difficult to estimate how much nitrogen is produced by legumes and micro-organisms; clovers in grassland may supply up to 250 kg/ha (200 units/acre) and micro-organisms about 60 kg/ha (50 units per acre) per annum.

*Phosphates* and *potash* are supplied by the soil minerals, organic manures and fertilizers.

The farmer has to decide each year what fertilizers to put on each crop. This is partly a haphazard choice and partly based on the results of experiments and his previous experience on his farm. Soil analysis, as at present carried out, gives no indication of nitrogen requirements, and is only a very rough guide to the need for phosphates and potash.

TABLE 6. NUTRIENTS REMOVED BY CROPS.

| Crop (good average yield) | N kg/ha | N lb/acre | P₂O₅ kg/ha | P₂O₅ lb/acre | K₂O kg/ha | K₂O lb/acre | |
|---|---|---|---|---|---|---|---|
| *Wheat* | | | | | | | If cereal straw is burnt on the field after combining, the potash is not lost but may be unevenly distributed. |
| grain 5 t/ha (40 cwt/acre) | 93 | 83 | 43 | 38 | 30 | 27 | |
| straw 5 t/ha (40 cwt/acre) | 17 | 15 | 7 | 6 | 40 | 36 | |
| Total | 110 | 98 | 50 | 44 | 70 | 63 | |
| *Barley* | | | | | | | |
| grain 4 t/ha (32 cwt/acre) | 67 | 60 | 33 | 30 | 22 | 20 | |
| straw 3 t/ha (24 cwt/acre) | 17 | 15 | 4 | 4 | 31 | 28 | |
| Total | 84 | 75 | 37 | 34 | 53 | 48 | |
| *Oats* | | | | | | | |
| grain 4 t/ha (32 cwt/acre) | 67 | 60 | 33 | 30 | 22 | 20 | |
| straw 5 t/ha (40 cwt/acre) | 15 | 13 | 9 | 8 | 74 | 66 | |
| Total | 82 | 73 | 42 | 38 | 96 | 86 | |
| *Potatoes* | | | | | | | The response to phosphatic fertilizers is greater than these figures suggest. |
| tubers 30 t/ha (12 tons/acre) | 101 | 90 | 45 | 40 | 179 | 160 | |
| dry haulm 2½ t/ha (1 ton/acre) | 50 | 45 | 6 | 5 | 112 | 100 | |
| Total | 151 | 135 | 51 | 45 | 291 | 260 | |
| *Sugar-beet* | | | | | | | If sugar-beet tops or kale are eaten by stock on the field where grown then most of the nutrients may be returned to the soil. |
| roots 40 t/ha (16 tons/acre) | 71 | 64 | 39 | 35 | 78 | 70 | |
| fresh tops 35 t/ha (14 tons/acre) | 119 | 106 | 39 | 35 | 202 | 180 | |
| Total | 190 | 170 | 78 | 70 | 280 | 250 | |
| *Kale* | | | | | | | |
| fresh crop 50 t/ha (20 tons/acre) | 224 | 200 | 67 | 60 | 202 | 180 | |

TABLE 7. THE NEED FOR AND EFFECTS OF NITROGEN, PHOSPHORUS, AND POTASSIUM.

| Plant nutrient | Crops which are most likely to suffer from deficiency | Field conditions where deficiency is likely to occur | Deficiency symptoms | Effect on crop growth | Effects of excess | Time and method of application |
|---|---|---|---|---|---|---|
| Nitrogen (N) | All farm crops except legumes (e.g. beans, peas, clover). It is especially important for leafy crops such as grasses, cereals kales and cabbages. | On all soils except peats, and especially where organic matter is low and after continuous cereal crops. | Thin, weak, spindly growth; lack of tillers and side shoots; small yellowish-green leaves, sometimes showing "autumn" tints. | Increases leaf size, rate of growth and yield. Produces darker green leaves. | Causes "lodging" of cereal crops. Delays ripening. Produces soft growth which is more susceptible to disease and frost. May spoil crop quality by lowering the starch or sugar content. If combine-drilled germination of seed may be damaged. | Nitrogen fertilizers applied in seed-bed or top-dressed in spring. Anhydrous ammonia may be injected about 6"–9" into the soil at up to 200 units/ac. to supply grass needs for 3–4 months. |

[continued overleaf

TABLE 7. THE NEED FOR AND EFFECTS OF NITROGEN, PHOSPHORUS, AND POTASSIUM—*continued*

| Plant nutrient | Crops which are most likely to suffer from deficiency | Field conditions where deficiency is likely to occur | Deficiency symptoms | Effect on crop growth | Effects of excess | Time and method of application |
|---|---|---|---|---|---|---|
| Phosphorus (P) | Root crops (e.g. sugar-beet, mangolds, swedes, carrots), clovers, lucerne, potatoes and kale. | Clay soils; acid soils —especially in high rainfall areas, chalk and limestone soils and peats. Poor grassland. | Similar to nitrogen except that leaves are a dull, bluish-green colour with purple or bronze tints. | Speeds up growth of seedlings and increases root develop-ment: hastens leaf growth and maturity. Encourages clover develop-ment in grassland. Improves quality of crops. | Might cause crops to ripen too early and so reduce yield if not balanced with nitrogen and potash fertilizers. | Phosphorus fertilizers applied in seed-bed for arable crops; "placement" in bands near or with the seed reduces the amount which has to be applied. Broadcast on grassland in autumn or early spring. |

TABLE 7. THE NEED FOR AND EFFECTS OF NITROGEN, PHOSPHORUS, AND POTASSIUM—*continued*

| Plant nutrient | Crops which are most likely to suffer from deficiency | Field conditions where deficiency is likely to occur | Deficiency symptoms | Effect on crop growth | Effects of excess | Time and method of application |
|---|---|---|---|---|---|---|
| Potassium (K) | Potatoes, carrots, beans, barley, clovers, lucerne, sugar-beet and mangolds. | Light sandy soils, chalk soils, peats, badly drained soils, grassland which has been repeatedly cut for hay, silage or "zero" grazing. | Growth is squat, and growing points "die-back", e.g. edges and tip of leaves die and appear scorched. | Crops are healthy and resist disease and frost better. Prolongs growth. Improves quality of crops. Balances nitrogen and phosphate fertilizers. | May delay ripening too much. May cause magnesium deficiency in fruit and glasshouse crops and "grass-staggers" in grazing animals. | Potassium fertilizers appplied in seed-bed for arable crops; "placement" in bands with or near the seed reduces the amount which has to be applied; care required amounts combine-drilled in dry seed-bed. Broadcast on grassland in autumn of late spring. |

Table 7 sets out the main needs for nitrogen, phosphorus and potassium, and also the effects of deficiency and excess.

The quantities of nitrogen, phosphate and potash used are usually expressed as *units*; average recommendations are given in the chapters dealing with individual crops.

## Units of Plant Food

A *unit* of plant food is 1% of 1 cwt (i.e. 1·12 lb). The metric equivalent unit might be 0·5 kg.

A nitrogen fertilizer containing 21% N has 21 units of nitrogen in each cwt (112 lb). Similarly, a compound fertilizer containing 10% N, 12% $P_2O_5$ and 16% $K_2O$ (usually given as 10:12:16) has 10 units of nitrogen, 12 units of phosphate and 16 units of potash in each cwt.

It is possible to compare the cost of fertilizers on a unit basis. For example:

Suppose   1 tonne of an ammonium nitrate fertilizer—e.g. "Nitram" (34·5% N)—costs £52 per ton net.

Then      1 cwt (50 kg) costs  $\dfrac{£52}{20}=£2·60,$

and so    1 unit of nitrogen in this fertilizer costs

$$\frac{2·6 \times 100}{34·5} = 7\tfrac{1}{2}\text{p approx.}$$

Also      suppose "nitro–chalk" (25% N) costs £40 per ton net.
Then      1 cwt costs £2·00,
and so    1 unit of nitrogen in this fertilizer costs

$$\frac{2·00 \times 100}{25} = 8\text{p.}$$

At these prices the "Nitram" is the best value.

If         1 ton of muriate of potash (60% $K_2O$) costs £60,
then     1 cwt costs £3·00,
and so    1 unit of $K_2O$ costs

$$\frac{3·00 \times 100}{60} = 5\text{p.}$$

Similarly, the cost of 1 unit of $P_2O_5$ is about 13p.

UNIT VALUES

These can be calculated as 1% of a cwt (see p. 94) or as 1% of a ton (as is usually done when calculating residual values—see p. 111).

## Straight Fertilizers

*Straight* fertilizers supply only one of the major plant foods.

NITROGEN FERTILIZERS (N)

The nitrogen in many straight and compound fertilizers is in the ammonium ($NH_4$ ions) form but this is quickly changed by bacteria in the soil to the nitrate ($NO_3$ ions) form. Many crop plants, e.g. cereals, take up and respond to the $NO_3$ ions quicker than the $NH_4$ ions but other crops, e.g. grass and potatoes, are equally responsive to $NH_4$ and $NO_3$ ions.

Commonly used nitrogen fertilizers are:

(1) *Ammonium nitrate*, $NH_4 NO_3$ (33·5–34·5% N). This is a very popular fertilizer for top-dressing (half the nitrogen is very readily available) and is marketed in a special prilled or granular form to resist moisture absorption. It has been used by guerillas to make bombs, but is safe if stored in sealed bags and well away from combustible organic matter. Heavy dressings tend to make the soil acid.

(2) *Ammonium nitrate lime* (21–26% N). These granular fertilizers are mixtures of ammonium nitrate and lime, sold under various trade names; they take up moisture readily when the bags are opened and go pasty; they do not cause acidity in the soil.

(3) *Urea* (45% N). This is the most concentrated solid nitrogen fertilizer and is marketed in prilled form; it is sometimes used for aerial top-dressing. In the soil, urea changes to ammonium carbonate which may temporarily cause a harmful local high pH. Nitrogen, as ammonia, may be lost from the surface of chalk or limestone soils, or light sandy soils when urea is applied as a top-dressing; when it is washed or worked into the soil it is as effective as any other nitrogen fertilizer; chemical and bacterial action changes it to ammonium and nitrate forms. If applied close to seeds, urea may reduce germination. It is also used to make plastics, and so it is expensive.

(4) *Sulphate of ammonia* (S/A), $(NH_4)_2.SO_4$. This was the main source of nitrogen, but is seldom used now. It consists of whitish, needle-like crystals and is produced as a by-product from gasworks or synthetically from atmospheric nitrogen. Bacteria change the ammonium nitrogen to nitrate. It has a greater acidifying action on the soil than other nitrogen fertilizers. Some nitrogen may be lost as ammonia when it is top-dressed on chalk soils.

(5) *Nitrate of soda*, $Na.NO_3$ (16% N) is obtained from natural deposits in Chile and usually marketed as moisture-resistant granules. The nitrogen is readily available and the sodium is of value to some crops such as sugar beet and mangels. It is expensive and so is not widely used.

(6) *Calcium nitrate* (15·5% N). This is a double salt of calcium nitrate and ammonium nitrate in prilled form. It is mainly used on the Continent.

(7) *Anhydrous ammonia* (82% N). This is ammonia gas liquefied under high pressure (up to 180 lb/sq in.), stored in special tanks and injected about 150 mm (6 in.) into the soil from pressurized tanks through tubes fitted at the back of strong tines; strict safety precautions must be observed. The ammonia is rapidly absorbed by the clay and organic matter in the soil and there is very little loss if the soil is in a friable condition and the slit made by the injection tine closes quickly. It is not advisable to use anhydrous ammonia on very wet or very cloddy soils or where there are lots of stones, but it can be injected when crops are growing, for example into winter wheat crops in spring, between rows of Brussels sprouts, and into grassland. The cost of application is much higher than for other fertilizers, but the material is cheap, so the applied cost per unit compares very favourably with other forms of nitrogen. On grassland it is usually applied twice—in spring and again in mid-summer—at up to 200 units per acre each time. In cold countries it can be applied in late autumn for the following season, but the mild periods in winters in this country usually cause heavy losses by nitrification and leaching.

(8) *Aqueous ammonia* (about 28% N). This is ammonia dissolved in water under slight pressure; it must be injected into the soil (100–120 mm), but the risk of losses is very much less than with the

anhydrous ammonia; also, cheaper equipment can be used.

(9) *Aqueous nitrogen solutions* (26–32% N). These are usually solutions of mixtures of ammonium nitrate and urea, and are commonly used on farm crops; they are not under pressure and can be sprayed on the soil. If injected or worked in they are just as effective as other nitrogen fertilizers, but there is a risk of some loss from surface applications to chalk and very sandy soils: they can be sprayed on growing cereals and grass with a slight risk of scorch damage which can be avoided by dribbling the solution through flexible polythene tubes (page 104, Liquid Fertilizers).

(10) *Gas liquor* (1·7% for "10 oz liquor")—a variable by-product from gasworks before North Sea gas was available; the nitrogen is mainly present as ammonium salts. It is likely to scorch growing crops and has been used as a combined top-dressing and selective herbicide to kill weeds such as charlock in kale (it contains phenolic substances) at about 33–55 hl/ha (300–500 gal/acre).

Various attempts have been made to produce slow-acting nitrogen fertilizers and reasonable results have been obtained with such products as resin-coated granules of ammonium nitrate (26% N), sulphur-coated urea prills (36% N) (bacteria slowly break down the yellow sulphur in the soil), and urea formaldehydes (30–40% N).

Organic fertilizers such as *Hoof and Horn* (13% N)—ground up hooves and horns of cattle, *Shoddy* (up to 15% N), waste from wool mills, and *Dried Blood* (10–13% N), a soluble quick-acting fertilizer, are usually too expensive for farm crops and are mainly used by horticulturists.

Much of the nitrogen now supplied to farm crops comes from compound fertilizers in which it is usually present as ammonium nitrate, ammonium phosphate, or urea.

PHOSPHATE FERTILIZERS (P)

By custom and by law the quality or grade of phosphate fertilizers is expressed as a percentage of phosphorus pentoxide ($P_2O_5$) equivalent.

(1) *Ground rock phosphate.* The natural rock ground to a fine powder—i.e. 90% should pass through a 100-mesh sieve (10,000

holes per square inch). The best ones contain about 29% $P_2O_5$ which is insoluble in water. They should only be used on acid soils in high rainfall areas and for grassland and brassica crops (e.g. swedes, turnips, kale).

*Hyperphosphate* is a softer rock phosphate obtained from North Africa. It can be ground to a very high degree of fineness, 90% passing through a 300-mesh sieve—48 holes/mm² (30,000 holes/in²). Because of this it will dissolve more quickly in the soil, although it should still only be used under the same conditions and for the same crops as ordinary ground rock phosphate.

(2) *Superphosphate* (super). This contains 18–21% water-soluble $P_2O_5$ produced by treating ground rock phosphate with sulphuric acid. It also contains gypsum ($CaSO_4$), which may remain as a white residue in the soil, and a small amount of unchanged rock phosphate. It is suitable for all crops and all soil conditions.

(3) *Triple superphosphate*. This contains about 47% water-soluble $P_2O_5$ and is produced by treating the rock phosphate with phosphoric acid. 1 cwt triple super = $2\frac{1}{2}$ cwt ordinary super.

(4) *Basic slags*. These are by-products in the manufacture of steel. The total amount of phosphate present varies between about 8–22% $P_2O_5$. This is insoluble in water but most of it may be soluble in a 2% citric acid solution (this is a guide to its solubility in the soil). A good slag should have a high percentage $P_2O_5$; a high proportion of this (80% +) should be *citric soluble* and over 80% should pass through a 100-mesh sieve—16 holes/mm² (10,000 holes per in.²). Slags are not so quick acting as "supers" and give best results on acid soils. Cattle may be poisoned by eating herbage recently treated with slag which has not been washed off the leaves. Rate of application 0·75–1·25 t/ha (6–10 cwt/acre). Slags contain some trace elements.

POTASH FERTILIZERS (K)

The quality or grade of potash fertilizers is expressed as a percentage of potassium oxide ($K_2O$) equivalent.

(1) *Muriate of potash* M/P (potassium chloride) as now sold usually

contains 60% $K_2O$. It does not store very well and does not spread easily unless specially treated. This is the commonest source of potash for farm use and for the manufacture of compounds containing potash.

(2) *Sulphate of potash* S/P (potassium sulphate). This is made from the muriate and so is more expensive per unit $K_2O$. It contains 48–50% $K_2O$ and is the best type to use for quality production of crops such as potatoes, tomatoes and other market garden crops.

(3) *Kainit and potash salts.* These are usually a mixture of potassium and sodium salts, and sometimes magnesium salts. They contain about 12–30% $K_2O$. They have most value for sugar-beet and similar crops for which the sodium is a useful plant food.

SALT

*Common salt* (sodium chloride) is a cheap and useful fertilizer for sugar-beet and similar crops—applied at the rate of $\frac{1}{2}$ tonne/ha (4 cwt/acre).

An increasing number of research workers, writers and advisers are now expressing amounts of plant nutrients in terms of the elements P(phosphorus) and K(potassium) instead of the commonly used oxide terms $P_2O_5$ and $K_2O$ respectively. Throughout this book the oxide terms are used but these can be converted to the element terms by using the following factors:

$$P_2O_5 \times 0.43 = P$$
$$K_2O \times 0.83 = K$$

e.g. 100 units of $P_2O_5$ = 43 units of P
100 units of $K_2O$ = 83 units of K

## Compound or Mixed Fertilizers

These fertilizers supply *two* or *three* of the major plant foods. (i.e. nitrogen, phosphorus and potassium). They are produced by mixing such fertilizers as ammonium nitrate, ammonium phosphate, and muriate of potash or by more complex chemical processes.

About 75% of all fertilizers now used in this country are compounds. These are *well mixed* by machinery, are *granulated* and *store well*. This is a great saving in labour at a busy time because fertilizers mixed on the farm do not store well.

The concentration of compounds varies widely; some recently introduced contain 60 units of plant food per cwt, e.g. 10% N, 25% $P_2O_5$, 25% $K_2O$. If fertilizers are mixed on the farm it is possible to calculate the analysis of the mixture as follows:

Suppose the following are mixed:

> 2 parts sulphate of ammonia,
> 3 parts superphosphate and
> 1 part muriate of potash.

|  | N | P | K |
|---|---|---|---|
| 200 kg of S/A (21%) contain | 42 kg | — | — |
| 300 kg of super (18%) contain | — | 54 kg | — |
| 100 kg of M/P (60%) contain | — | — | 60 kg |

| | N | P | K |
|---|---|---|---|
| 600 kg of the mixture contain | 42 kg | 54 kg | 60 kg |
| 100 kg of the mixture contain | 7 kg | 9 kg | 10 kg |

The analysis of the mixture is therefore 7:9:10.

Purchased compound fertilizers usually cost about £4·00–£5·00 more per ton than the equivalent in "straights".

### Plant Food Ratios

Fertilizers containing different amounts of plant food may have the same plant food ratios. For example:

| | Fertilizer | Ratio | Equivalent rates of application |
|---|---|---|---|
| (a) | 12:12:18 | 1:1:1½ | 5 parts of (a) = 4 parts of (b) |
| (b) | 15:15:23 | 1:1:1½ | |

(c) 15:10:10    1½:1:1    7 parts of (c) = 5 parts of (d)
(d) 21:14:14    1½:1:1
(e) 12:18:12    1:1½:1    5 parts of (e) = 6 parts of (f)
(f) 10:15:10    1:1½:1

Some examples of compounds and possible uses:

| Compound (N:P:K) | Crop | Rate | | Kg/ha and (units/ac) | | |
|---|---|---|---|---|---|---|
| | | 50 kg bags/ ha | cwt bags/ acre | N | P | K |
| 12:12:18 | potatoes | 25 | 10 | 150 (120) | 150 (120) | 225 (180) |
| 20:10:10 | spring cereal | 10 | 4 | 100 ( 80) | 50 ( 40) | 50 ( 40) |
| 0:20:20 | autumn cereal | 5 | 2 | 0 | 50 ( 40) | 50 ( 40) |
| 9:25:25 | autumn cereal | 5 | 2 | 22 ( 18) | 60 ( 50) | 60 ( 50) |

Fertilizers are supplied in various ways:

*Solids*

(a) 50 kg (1 cwt) five-ply *paper bags* (becoming out-dated).
(b) 50 kg (1 cwt) *polythene bags*. These can be stored outside but should be covered with a polythene sheet. If stored on pallets the manual work of handling is considerably reduced.
(e) *Bulk*—can be stored in dry, concrete bays covered with polythene sheets. 1 tonne (ton) occupies about 1 m³ (35 ft³). It can be moved by tractor hydraulic loaders or augers into trailers or trailer spreaders. It may also be supplied to the field as required in self-unloading 2 tonne (ton) bins.

*Liquids.* In the last six years there has been more than a 120% increase in the use of liquids compared with a 15% increase in the same period of solid fertilizers. The dominantly arable counties show that liquid nitrogen has an 18% share of the market, and liquid compounds 8·5% of the total tonnage of compound fertilizers used.

Because, compared with solids, liquid fertilizers are easier, quicker and cheaper to handle and apply, a further increase in their use must be considered inevitable.

Liquid fertilizers are simple non-pressurized solutions of normal solid fertilizer raw materials. They should be distinguished from pressurized solutions such as aqueous ammonia (page 98) and, more particularly, anhydrous ammonia (page 98). Liquids are stored in steel tanks on the farm, and the application equipment for broadcasting the fertilizer can also be used for herbicides and pesticides. Special equipment has now been developed for injecting the fertilizer for the potato and brassica crops, and a combine-drill attachment is now in use for sowing the liquid and cereal together. For top-dressing, and to minimize scorch, the dribble-bar technique, whereby the liquid is applied to the crop through trailing pipes from the boom, is now being used by some farmers.

At present, liquid compounds are only about half as concentrated as the solid compound, but because the fertilizer is pumped rather than handled in bags, this is of little consequence.

The unit cost of the plant food is similar to that of the solid, and there is no difference in subsequent plant growth following the application of the fertilizer in a liquid or solid form.

## Application of Fertilizers

The main methods used are:

(a) *Broadcast distributors* using various mechanisms such as:

(1) *"Plate and flicker" type*. Revolving saucer-shaped discs at the bottom of the hopper carry fertilizer to the front or the rear of the box where it is flicked off by swiftly revolving fingers. This is one of the most accurate types of distributor.

(2) Other types involving rollers, brushes, chains, etc.

(3) *Spinning disc* types. These may be mounted or semi-mounted on the three-point tractor linkage or may be trailer types. Accuracy of distribution varies considerably, and is very dependent on accurate setting and amount of overlap.

(b) *Combine drills*. Fertilizer and seed (e.g. cereals) from separate hoppers is fed down the same or an adjoining spout. A *star-wheel* feed mechanism is normally used for the fertilizer and this usually produces a "dollop" effect along the rows. In soils low in phosphate and potash this method of *placement* of the fertilizer is much more efficient than broadcasting.

(c) *Placement drills*. These machines usually place the fertilizer in bands 60 mm (2–3 in.) to the side and 40 mm (1–2 in.) below the rows of seeds. It is more efficient than broadcasting for crops such as peas, and also sugar-beet on some soils, e.g. sandy soils. Other types of placement drills attached to the planter are used for applying fertilizers to the potato crop.

(d) *Broadcast from aircraft*. This is useful for top-dressing of cereals —especially in a wet spring; also for applying fertilizers in inaccessible areas such as hill grazings. Highly concentrated fertilizers should be used, e.g. urea.

(e) Liquids injected under pressure into the soil.

(f) Liquids (non-pressurized) broadcast or injected.

MACHINERY MAINTENANCE

*All machinery for fertilizer application should be thoroughly washed after use and coated with a rust-proofing material during long idle periods.*

## Organic Manures

FARMYARD MANURE (F.Y.M.)

This consists of dung and urine, and the litter used for bedding stock. It is not a standardized product, and its value depends on:

(1) *The kind of animal that makes it*. If animals are fed strictly according to maintenance and production requirements, the quality of dung produced by various classes of stock will be similar. But in practice it is generally found that as cows and young stock utilize much of the nitrogen and phosphate in their food, their dung is poorer than that produced by fattening stock.

(2) *The kind of food fed to the animal that makes the dung*. The richer the food in protein and minerals, the richer will be the dung.

But it is uneconomical to feed a rich diet just to produce a richer dung.

(3) *The amount of straw used.* The less straw used, the more concentrated will be the manure and the more rapidly will it break down to a "short" friable condition.

Straw is the best type of litter available, although bracken, peat moss, sawdust and wood shavings can be used. About 1·5 tonne (tons) of straw per animal is needed in a covered yard for 6 months, and between 2–3 tonne in a semi-covered or open yard.

(4) *The manner of storage.* There can be considerable losses from F.Y.M. because of bad storage.

Dung from cowsheds, cubicles and milking parlours should, if possible, be put into a heap which is protected from the elements to prevent the washing out and dilution of a large percentage of the plant foods which it contains. Dung made in yards should preferably remain there until it is spread on the land, and then, to prevent further loss, it is advisable to plough it in immediately.

F.Y.M. is important chiefly because of the valuable physical effects on the soil of the humus it contains. It is also a very valuable source of plant foods, particularly nitrogen, phosphate and potash, as well as other elements in smaller amounts. Ten tons of well-made F.Y.M. contain approximately 125 kg (100 units) N, 75 kg (60 units) $P_2O_5$ and 125 kg (100 units) $K_2O$. Much of the nitrogen may be lost before it is ploughed in and all the plant food in F.Y.M. is less readily available than that in chemical fertilizers.

*Application.* The application of F.Y.M. will be dealt with under the various crops.

LIQUID MANURE, AND SLURRY

With the introduction of more intensive livestock enterprises, the rising cost of straw for bedding, and the need for cheap and effective mechanical methods of dealing with animal excreta, more and more farmers are now dealing with manure in a liquid or semi-solid (slurry) form instead of the traditional solid form as produced in straw-bedded yards. However, in many cases this change has created more problems than it has solved, for example—this slurry must not be allowed to pollute watercourses; also, trouble can arise from the nuisance of smells and possible health hazards over a wide area when the slurry is diluted and distributed by rain-guns as organic irrigation. These problems and that of silage effluent are dealt with in detail in M.A.F.F. leaflets nos. 44 (Slurry handling) 67 (Farm waste disposal).

The approximate amounts of excreta (faeces and urine) produced by various types of stock are set out below:

| Livestock | Daily amounts of excreta produced | | |
|---|---|---|---|
| | kg or litres | lb | gal |
| Dairy cows 550–600 kg (11–12 cwt), e.g. cubicles and self-fed silage | 45 | 100 | 10 |
| Fattening cattle 400–500 kg (8–10 cwt), e.g. cubicles or slatted floors | 36 | 80 | 8 |
| Fattening pigs 75 kg (165 lb) | 4·5 | 10 | 1 |
| 10,000 laying hens | 1360 | 3000 | 300 |

The fresh excreta from these animals may be spread, from a rota-spreader type of manure spreader, or, as is usually the case, it is diluted with washing or rain water and can then be spread from a vacuum or mechanically loaded slurry tanker or pumped through a rain-gun after dilution of 1 part manure to 2 parts of water.

The amount of plant nutrients in slurry will vary according to the rations fed and will also depend on how it is stored, e.g. some nitrogen may be lost into the air. However, the approximate nutrient value to crops of slurry of average quality is set out below:

*Available* nutrients in *one tonne* (ton) i.e. 1000 kg or litres (220 gal) of *undiluted* slurry.

|  | N | | $P_2O_5$ | | $K_2O$ | |
|---|---|---|---|---|---|---|
|  | kg | units | kg | units | kg | units |
| Cattle (faeces and urine) | 5 | 10 | 1·5 | 3 | 4·5 | 9 |
| Pigs (faeces and urine) | 4·5 | 9 | 4·5 | 9 | 4 | 8 |
| Poultry (fresh manure) | 11 | 22 | 11 | 22 | 5·5 | 11 |

If this is diluted 1:1 (for tanker distribution) then divide above figures by 2. If diluted 1:2 (for rain-gun distribution) then divide by 3.

The rates of application to a field will vary for many reasons, for example, if applied to a "sacrifice" field in winter prior to sowing kale or a ley mixture the amount need not be limited (within reason) provided it does not run off into the drains and ditches. If applied before planting cereals, not more than 20 metre³/hectare (1800 gal/acre) of undiluted cattle or pig slurry should be used (this rate of application could be applied by a rain-gun (using 1:2 dilution) in about 25–30 minutes). Higher rates might be used before root crops. On grassland, care must be taken that the sward is not killed by too thick a covering of slurry and the season should also be considered. A 30 minute setting of a rain-gun, say 33 m³/hectare (3000 gal/acre), is possible in winter, but, during the grazing season, each setting should be limited to 10–15 minutes otherwise prolonged tainting of the sward will upset the grazing routine.

On free-draining soil, if slurry is pushed over a ramp into a heap which is contained by a wall of straw bales and netting wire, or railway sleepers, most of the liquid will soak away or evaporate and during the following summer it is usually dry enough to be lifted with a fore-end loader into F.Y.M. spreaders. This drier material may have double the percentage of nutrients as that of the fresh manure.

The excreta from cows on a "straw-balancer" feeding system is much more solid than that from cows on a self-feed silage system.

Soak-away ditches, pits and lagoons may also be used for disposal of excreta and washing water but these may require to be cleaned out occasionally.

The very high price of fertilizers makes it highly desirable that the valuable nutrients in organic manures should be utilized as fully as possible. This is best achieved if the slurry or other material is applied at a time when growing crops can utilize it, and so storage is usually necessary. Many dairy farmers are now storing slurry in lagoons or pits which can be emptied in late spring or summer; this material can then be applied to grass fields or to fields which will be reseeded or planted with kale.

## CEREAL STRAWS

Straw is a valuable source of organic matter, although its plant food content is low. By ploughing-in straw on poor, light soils, the soil structure is improved. On these poor soils, it is advisable to apply 25 kg (20 units) N for every ton of straw ploughed in to supply the needs of the bacteria which rot down the straw. On fertile soils the nitrogen is unnecessary.

But there are practical difficulties in the ploughing-in of straw. It must be spread evenly; ideally it should be chopped, and good ploughing is necessary to bury it. Because of all this, unwanted straw is often burnt unless it can be sold at a reasonable price.

## THE LEY

When a field is put down to grass, fertility and soil structure are improved, and this increased fertility can be utilized by a succession of arable crops before the field is put back again to grass. This is the alternate husbandry system of farming and it has for many years formed the basis of mixed arable and livestock farming in this country.

Work at Experimental Stations and some of the Ministry Experimental Husbandry Farms (i.e. on different soil types) questions the validity of this system of farming as experiments over the last twelve years show that increase in arable crop yields following grass is very slight compared with twelve years' continuous arable where diseases and pests are not limiting factors.

GREEN MANURING

This is the practice of growing and ploughing in green crops to increase the organic matter content of the soil. It is normally only carried out on light soils.

White mustard is the most commonly grown crop. Sown at 9–17 kg/ha (8–15 lb/acre) it can produce a crop ready for ploughing within 6–8 weeks. It can also provide useful cover for pheasants. Leguminous crops such as vetches are also sometimes grown.

But green manuring does not appreciably increase the organic matter in the soil. It is a rather unsatisfactory substitute for F.Y.M., straw and the ley.

SEAWEED

Seaweed is often used instead of F.Y.M. for crops such as early potatoes in coastal areas, e.g. Ayrshire, Cornwall and the Channel Islands. Ten tonne (tons) contain about 50 kg (100 units) of N, 10 kg (20 units) $P_2O_5$ and 140 kg (280 units) $K_2O$. It also contains about 164 kg (360 lb) of salt. The organic matter in seaweed breaks down rapidly.

POULTRY MANURE

The composition varies according to where it has been produced and stored. When partly dried it can be handled as F.Y.M., or, it may be treated as slurry after mixing with water.

Poultry manure is relatively deficient in potash.

WASTE ORGANIC MATERIALS

Various waste products are used for market garden crops— partly as a source of organic matter and partly because they release

| Source | Average amounts per tonne (ton) | | | | | |
| --- | --- | --- | --- | --- | --- | --- |
| | N | | P$_2$O$_5$ | | K$_2$O | |
| | kg | units | kg | units | kg | units |
| Fresh manure, e.g. from battery cages | 20 | 40 | 20 | 40 | 8 | 16 |
| Air-dried manure | 35 | 70 | 35 | 70 | 15 | 30 |
| Straw yards | 6 | 12 | 4 | 8 | 6 | 12 |
| Deep litter | 20 | 40 | 25 | 50 | 15 | 30 |

nitrogen slowly to the crop. They are usually too expensive for ordinary farm crops.

*Shoddy* (waste wool and cotton) contains 50–150 kg (100–300 units) of nitrogen per tonne (ton). Waste wool is best, and is applied at 2·5–5 tonne/ha (1–2 tons/acre.)

*Dried blood*, ground *hoof and horn* and *meat and bone meal* are also used; the nitrogen composition is variable.

### Residual Values of Fertilizers and Manures

The nutrients in most manures and fertilizers are not used up completely in the year of application. The amount likely to remain for use in the following years is taken into account when compensating outgoing farm tenants.

All the *nitrogen* in *soluble* nitrogen fertilizers (e.g. sulphate of ammonia, nitro-chalk, compounds, and in dried blood) is used in the first year.

For *nitrogen* in bones, hoof and horn, meat and bone meal:
Allow $\frac{1}{2}$ after one crop and $\frac{1}{4}$ after two crops.
*Phosphate* in *soluble* form, e.g. super, basic slag, compounds:
Allow $\frac{2}{3}$ after one crop, $\frac{1}{3}$ after two and $\frac{1}{8}$ after three crops.
*Phosphate* in *insoluble* form, e.g. bones, ground rock phosphate:
Allow $\frac{1}{3}$ after one crop, $\frac{1}{6}$ after two and $\frac{1}{12}$ after three.
*Potash*, e.g. muriate or sulphate of potash, compounds:
Allow $\frac{1}{2}$ after one crop and $\frac{1}{4}$ after two.

*Lime:* one-eighth of the cost is subtracted each year after application.

## Suggestions for Classwork

(1) Examine samples of all the commonly used "straight" fertilizers and a few compounds and note differences between them.
(2) Visit experimental farms or demonstration plots to see the differences in crop growth due to deficient, excess and correct supply of nutrients.
(3) If possible, visit farms to see bulk and sack storage of fertilizers, methods of handling and application.
(4) When visiting farms note the various methods used for handling F.Y.M. and slurry.

# CHAPTER 4

# CROPPING

## Climate and Weather and their Effects on Cropping

*Climate* has an important influence on the type of crops which can be grown satisfactorily nearly every year. It may be defined as a seasonal average of the many *weather* conditions.

*Weather* is the state of the atmosphere at any time—it is the combined effect of such conditions as heat or cold, wetness or dryness, wind or calm, clearness or cloudiness, pressure and the electric state of the air.

The daily, monthly and yearly changes of temperature and rainfall give a fairly good indication of the conditions likely to be found.

Average yearly figures such as 1000 mm rainfall and temperature 10°C are of very limited value.

The climate of this country is mainly influenced by:

(1) its distance from the equator (50–60°N latitude),
(2) the warm Gulf Stream which flows along the western coasts.
(3) the prevailing south-west winds,
(4) the numerous "lows" or "depressions" which cross from west to east and bring most of the rainfall,
(5) the distribution of highland and lowland—most of the hilly and mountainous areas are on the west side,
(6) its nearness to the continent of Europe; from there hot winds in summer and very cold winds in winter can affect the weather in the southern and eastern areas.

Local variations are caused by *altitude, aspect* and *slope*.

*Altitude* (height above sea level) can affect climate in many ways. The temperature drops about 0·5°C (1°F) for every 90 m (300 ft) rise above sea level. Every 15m (50 ft) rise in height usually shortens the growing season by 2 days (one in spring and one in autumn) and it may check the rate of growth during the year. High land is more likely to be buffeted by strong winds and is likely to receive more rain from the moisture-laden prevailing winds which are cooled as they rise upwards.

*Aspect* (the direction in which land faces) can affect the amount of sunshine (heat) absorbed by the soil. In this country the temperature of north-facing slopes may be 1°C (2°F) lower than on similar slopes facing south.

*Slope.* When air cools down it becomes heavier and will move down a slope and force warmer air upwards. This is why frost often occurs on the lowest ground on clear still nights whereas the upper slopes may remain free of frost. "Frost pockets" occur where cold air collects in hollows or alongside obstructing banks, walls, hedges, etc. (see Fig. 35). Frost-susceptible crops such as early potatoes, maize and fruit should not be grown in such places.

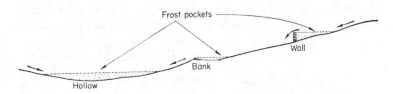

FIG. 35. Diagram to show how frost pockets are formed as cold air flows down a slope.

### RAINFALL IN THE BRITISH ISLES

This comes mainly from the moist south-westerly winds and from the many "lows" or "depressions" which cross from west to east.

Western areas receive much more rain than eastern areas—partly because of the west to east movement of the rain-bearing air and partly because most of the high land is along the western side of the country.

The average annual rainfall on lowland areas in the west is about 900 mm (35 in.) and in the east is about 600 mm (24 in.). It is much greater on higher land.

## TEMPERATURE OF THE BRITISH ISLES

The temperature changes are mainly due to:

(1) the seasonal changes in length of day and intensity of sunlight
(2) the source of the wind, e.g. whether it is a mild south-westerly, or whether it is cold polar air from the north or from the continent in winter,
(3) local variations in altitude and aspect,
(4) night temperatures are usually higher when there is cloud cover which prevents too much heat escaping into the upper atmosphere.

The soil temperature may also be affected by colour—dark soils absorb more heat than light-coloured soils. Also, damp soils can absorb more heat than dry soils.

The average January temperature in lowland areas along the west side of the country is about 6°C (42°F) and about 4°C (39°F) along the east side.

The average July temperatures in lowland areas in the southern counties is about 17°C (62°F) but this drops to about 13°C (55°F) in the north of Scotland.

## CROPPING IN THE BRITISH ISLES

Grass grows well in the wetter, western areas and so dairying, stock rearing and fattening can be successfully carried on in these areas.

The drier areas in the east are best suited to arable crops which require fairly dry weather for easy harvesting.

The mild, frost-free areas in the south-west of England and Wales (i.e. parts of Devon, Cornwall, and Pembroke) are suitable for early crops of potatoes, broccoli, flowers, etc. The Isle of Thanet

(Kent) and the Ayrshire coast are also early areas free from late frosts.

The more exposed hill and mountain areas are unsuitable for intensive production because of the lower temperatures, very high rainfall, inaccessibility and steep slopes. These are mainly rough grazings used for extensive cattle and sheep rearing. Large areas are now forestry plantations.

Most of the chalk and oolitic limestone areas (in the south and east) are now used for large scale cereal production—particularly barley. The leys grown in these areas are mainly used by dairy cattle or sheep, or for herbage seed production. Cereals are grown on all types of soil. Maincrop potatoes and root crops, such as sugar-beet, are grown on the deeper loamy soils of the midlands and eastern counties. Carrots are grown on some light soils in the eastern counties.

Mixed farming (i.e. both crop and stock enterprises on the same farm) is found on most lowland farms. The proportion of grass (and so stock) to arable crops usually varies according to soil type and rainfall. The heavier soils and high rainfall areas usually have more grass than arable crops.


### Rotations

A *rotation* is a cropping system in which two or more crops are grown in a fixed sequence. If the rotation includes a period in grass, (a ley), which is used for grazing and conservation, the system is sometimes called "alternate husbandry" or mixed farming. The term "ley farming" describes a system where a farm or group of fields is cropped entirely with leys which are re-seeded at regular intervals; some people describe any cropping system which includes leys as "ley farming".

Farm crops may be grouped as follows:

(a) *Cereals* (*wheat, barley, oats* and *rye*). These are *exhaustive* crops because they are removed from the field and usually sold off the farm (i.e. they are cash crops). They encourage weeds—especially grass weeds such as couch. If grown continuously on the same field, fungous diseases such as take-all and eyespot, or pests such as eel-worms can seriously reduce yields. Continuous spring barley crops are least likely to suffer losses. Cereals have peak demands for labour in autumn (ploughing and some sowing), spring (sowing) and late summer (harvesting). Large-scale mechanization has greatly simplified cereal production.

(b) *Potatoes* and *root crops* such as *sugar-beet, mangolds, carrots,* etc. These are mainly high value cash crops and require deep soils. They have heavy demands for plant nutrients but allow the farmer to use large amounts of fertilizers and F.Y.M. and so build up fertility. Timely cultivations before sowing and during the early growth period can control most troublesome weeds—hence the reason for regarding this group as "cleaning" crops. This is expensive and chemical weed control is being introduced. It is very risky to grow any of these crops continuously—mainly because of eel-worms. This group has a high labour demand—especially for harvesting of potatoes and singling of sugar-beet. However, mechanization has solved many of the problems.

(c) *Pulse crops*, e.g. *peas* and *beans*. In many ways these crops resemble cereals but they can build up nitrogen in the nodules on their roots. They should not be grown continuously because of build-up of fungous diseases (e.g. clover and bean stem rot) and pests (e.g. pea root eelworm). They can provide a break from continuous cereal growing.

(d) *Restorative crops*, i.e. the crops which are usually fed off on the fields and so return nutrients and organic matter to the soil.

The best examples are *leys, kale* and *roots for folding off.*

A good crop rotation would include several crops because this would:

(1) reduce the financial risk if one crop yielded or sold badly,
(2) spread the labour requirements more evenly over the year,
(3) reduce the risk of diseases and pests associated with single cropping (mono-culture),

(4) probably give better control of weeds,
(5) provide more interest for the farmer.

However, most of these objectives could be obtained without having a rigid system of cropping. The present tendency is to break away from traditional systems and to simplify the cropping programme as much as possible.

This approach has been encouraged by:

(1) the need to economize in labour and capital expenditure,
(2) better machinery for growing and harvesting crops,
(3) much better control of pests and diseases—mainly by chemicals and resistant varieties,
(4) chemical weed control,
(5) guaranteed price systems for most crops.

Many well tried rotations have been practised in various parts of the country. One of the earliest and best known was the *Norfolk Four-Course* rotation which was well suited to arable areas in Eastern England.

It started as:

| | | |
|---|---|---|
| *Turnips* or *swedes* | Folded off with sheep in winter. | Roots |
| *Spring barley* (undersown) | Cash crop. | Cereal |
| *Red clover* | Grazed in spring and summer. | Ley |
| *Winter wheat* | Cash crop. | Cereal |

This was a well balanced rotation for:

(1) building up and maintenance of soil fertility,
(2) control of weeds and pests,
(3) employment of labour throughout the year,
(4) providing a reasonable profit.

However, considerable changes have occurred over the years mainly due to:

(1) the introduction of fertilizers, other crops and better machinery,

(2) greater freedom of cropping for tenant farmers,
(3) the need for increased profits.

Some of the *changes* which have occurred are:

(1) *Sugar-beet, potatoes, mangolds,* and *carrots* have replaced all or part of the folded roots.
(2) *Beans* and *peas* have replaced red clover in some areas or alternatively a two- or three-year *ley* has been introduced.
(3) Two or three successive cereal crops have replaced the barley and wheat crops.

An example of a wide variation is:

| | |
|---|---|
| Winter wheat | |
| 1 or 2 crops of spring barley | } Replacing winter wheat. |
| Sugar-beet or potatoes | Root break. |
| 1–3 cereal crops | Replacing spring barley. |
| 2–4-year ley | Replacing 1-year red clover ley. |

Where there is a big difference in the types of soil on a farm it may be advisable to have one rotation for the heavy soils and another for the light soils.

The most suitable rotation or cropping programme for a farm must be based on the management plan for the farm. It should provide grazing and other foods for the livestock and also the maximum possible acreage of cash crops. The cash crops grown will partly depend on the amount of labour available throughout the year.

### Continuous Cereal Production and "Break" Crops

Continuous cereal production has become an increasingly common system of farming on a wide range of soil types and climatic conditions. In many cases the whole farm is producing cereals whilst on other farms only certain fields are continuously in corn.

The main reasons for this are:

(a) simplification, and relatively low labour and capital requirements compared with root crops and livestock enterprises;
(b) greatly improved methods of harvesting, drying and storing grain;
(c) development of chemicals which give good weed control;
(d) reasonably profitable system.

Barley is the commonest cereal used for continuous cropping—mainly on loams and lighter types of soil—whilst continuous winter wheat has been increasing on heavy soils. Oat crops are not grown continuously because of their susceptibility to cyst (root) eelworm.

Many farmers are now justifiably worried about the long-term prospects of continuous cereal production because—

(1) Yields are not increasing sufficiently to maintain profits as costs rise—even where low-cost streamlined systems are used.
(2) Fungous diseases such as take-all and eyespot (see Table 22) and pests such as cyst (root) eelworm have been building up in the soil and seriously affecting yields in many cases. Take-all and cyst eelworms attack the roots of the cereal whereas eyespot attacks the stems (straw) a few inches above the soil. The general effect is to interfere with the normal absorption or translocation of water and nutrients, especially nitrogen and magnesium, with disastrous effects on the grain yield of individual plants. Also, they cause early ripening, or death, of the infected plants, and these are easily spotted in the crop as the season advances.
(3) Grass weeds are not being adequately controlled and these reduce yields by competition and as hosts of take-all and eyespot.
(4) Leaf diseases such as *yellow* and *black rusts* of wheat, *leaf blotch* (rhyncosporium) of barley, *crown rust* of oats and *mildew* of wheat, barley and oats can seriously reduce yields by inter-

fering with photosynthesis in the upper (flag) leaf and the ear where most of the carbohydrate in the grain is produced. These fungous diseases are spread by air-borne spores from neighbouring crops, from over-wintering crops or plants which have developed from shed grain at harvest time; they are increasing in importance due to the large increase in the area of cereals on all ploughable land, and carelessness in allowing self-sown plants to grow unhindered.

Where there is a need to increase the profitability of a farm and adequate capital is available then high value cash crops such as sugar-beet, potatoes or vining peas and beans may be introduced (if the soil depth and texture is suitable) or *leys* may be grown for stocking with dairy or beef cattle or sheep. In many cases adequate capital is not available for such enterprises and so other crops are being tried which give a "break" from continuous corn but can be grown, harvested and dried with the cereal machinery. Such crops are *beans, threshed peas, oil-seed rape, linseed, maize* and *seed crops of grass, clover* and *sugar-beet*.

A good "break" crop should provide at least as good an income as the cereal area it replaces: it should not allow weeds to spread; and, it should allow a crop of winter wheat to follow so that the farm income can be improved.

The crop of wheat following a "break" crop usually yields very well but the following one or two crops usually yield less than the average before the "break" crop and this raises doubts about the value of a "break" crop unless it gives a better profit than the cereal it replaces.

In a continuous barley system, eyespot is the most likely cause of trouble because barley is fairly resistant to take-all and cyst eelworm. Consequently, oats, which are resistant to eyespot, or an eyespot-resistant variety of wheat (see N.I.A.B. list) may be introduced occasionally—say once every 5 or 6 years—to increase the farm income because such oats or wheat crops usually yield over 5 tonne/ha (2 tons/acre) where the average barley yield is about 3·5 tonne/ha (28 cwt/acre).

## Catch Cropping

This is the practice of taking a quick growing crop between two major crops. With the dairy herd and sheep flock it can be very profitable provided:

(1) It does not interefere with the following main crop. This can happen when the main crop is planted late in a badly prepared seed-bed.

(2) The catch crop is not grown when more attention should have been given to cleaning the land of weeds.

(3) It is grown cheaply, without expensive seed-bed preparation, and with limited use of fertilizers, except possibly nitrogen.

There is now an increasing interest in catch-cropping, chiefly through the development of direct-drilling the autumn stubble with crops such as rape and the continental turnips.

Direct-drilling (page 80) has the advantage of conserving what moisture there is available in the soil at that time of the year. This helps to establish the catch crop that much more quickly.

Broadcasting gives a better cover and it should still be contemplated in the wetter areas.

*Examples of catch-cropping*

(1) Main crop   Winter barley.

Catch crop   For feeding until Christmas, continental stubble-turnips such as LEBRA, DEBRA, close-drilled at 2·5 kg/ha (2–4 lb/acre) or broadcast at 8 kg/ha (7 lb/acre); more frost-resistant crops such as the English Yellow varieties should be grown for feeding in the new year.

Main crop   Spring cereal or Kale.

(2) Main crop   Cereal undersown.

Catch crop   Italian ryegrass at 22–33 kg/ha (20–30 lb/acre).

This grass can provide:

(a) stubble-grazing,

(b) first bite (see Table 15),

(c) possibly another grazing or silage before
planting.

Main crop    Kale.

(3) Main crop    2nd early potatoes (harvested in July) or a ley
(ploughed in July).

Catch crop    Rye (e.g. Lovaszpatonai) at 190 kg/ha (1½ cwt/acre)
and Italian ryegrass at 11 kg/ha (10 lb/acre) to
provide:

(a) possibly an autumn graze (depending upon the
season),

(b) first bite,

(c) silage before planting.

Main crop    Kale.

(4) Main crop    Winter wheat, undersown in autumn with

Catch crop    3–4 kg/ha (3–4 lb/ac) Italian ryegrass.
This will produce and shed seed before harvest
and this usually provides:

(a) early bite,

(b) possibly another grazing, or silage cut before
planting,

Main crop    Roots or kale.

### Cereals

The *cereal* (*corn*, or *grain*) crops grown in this country are *wheat*,
*barley*, *oats*, *rye* and *maize*. Wheat and barley are the most important.

The introduction of combine-drills, combine-harvesters, driers,
and bulk handling has greatly simplified and improved cereal
production. Weeds can be controlled fairly easily by selective
chemicals—see chapter on "Weed Control".

These crops are easily recognized by their well known *ears*
(flowering heads). They can be recognized in the early, leafy stages
as shown in Fig. 36.

Although it is common practice now to use *weight* measures for
seed rates and yields of cereals, *volume* measures (e.g. bushel and
sack) are still used in some areas. The following table gives a comparison for average quality grain.

TABLE 8

| | Wheat | Barley | Oats | Rye |
|---|---|---|---|---|
| Peck (2 gal) | 15 lb | 14 lb | 10½ lb | 14 lb |
| Bushel (4 pecks) | 60 lb | 56 lb | 42 lb | 56 lb |
| Sack or coomb (4 bushels) | 2¼ cwt | 2 cwt | 1½ cwt | 2 cwt |
| Quarter (2 sacks) | 4½ cwt | 4 cwt | 3 cwt | 4 cwt |
| Weight per cubic foot | 50 lb | 44 lb | 32 lb | 44 lb |
| Cubic feet per ton | 46 | 51 | 70 | 51 |
| Weight per metre³ | 750 kg | 705 kg | 513 kg | 705 kg |
| Cubic metre per tonne | 1·25 | 1·41 | 1·95 | 1·41 |
| Kilogramme/hectolitre | 75 | 70 | 52·5 | 70 |

*Harvesting. Threshing* is the separation of the grains from the ears and straw. In *wheat* and *rye* the chaff is easily removed from the grain. In *barley*, only the awns are removed from the grain—the husk remains firmly attached to the kernel. In *oats* each grain kernel is surrounded by a husk which is fairly easily removed by a rolling process—as in the production of oatmeal; the chaff enclosing the grains in each spikelet threshes off. Most cereal crops in all parts of the country are now harvested by combine. The grain is bulk handled on most of the larger farms and stored in silos or loose on barn floors. Storage in *sacks* is still used on some farms.

Methods used for *drying* are set out below with usual moisture extraction rates in brackets:

(1) Various types of *continuous-flow driers:* hot air takes out the excess moisture (6% per hour) and fresh air then cools the grain but this may not be sufficient cooling in very hot weather.

(2) *Batch driers:* drying similar to (1) but the grain is held in batches in special containers during the drying process (6% per hour in small types; 6% per day in silo types).

(3) *Ventilated silos or bins:* cold or slightly heated air is blown through the grain in the silo—this can be a slow process, especially in damp weather (⅓–1% per day).

(4) *Sack driers:* heated air is blown through the sacks of grain laid

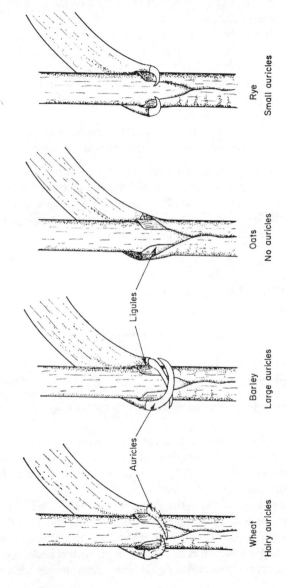

FIG. 36. Diagrams showing method of recognizing cereals in the leafy (vegetative) stage.

Wheat
Hairy auricles

Barley
Large auricles

Oats
No auricles

Rye
Small auricles

Auricles

Ligules

over holes in a platform or stacked to form a tunnel (1% per hour).

(5) *Floor drying:* a large volume of cold or slightly heated air is blown through the grain to remove excess moisture. The air may enter the grain in several ways, e.g.

(a) from ducts about a metre apart on or in the floor,
(b) from a single duct in the centre of a large heap (Rainthorpe system),
(c) through a perforated floor which may also be used to blow the grain to an outlet conveyor when emptying.

Floor drying is becoming increasingly popular because it can be done in a general-purpose building, it is a cheap method and requires very little labour when filling. Rate of drying $\frac{1}{3}$–1% per day.

Grain intended for the following purposes should not be heated above the following *maximum* temperatures:

| | |
|---|---|
| For seed, malting barley up to 24% m.c. | 49°C (120°F). |
| For seed, malting barley above 24% m.c. | 43°C (110°F). |
| Milling for human consumption e.g. wheatflour | 66°C (150°F). |
| For stock feeding | 82°C (180°F). |

Safe moisture contents for storage of all grains:

| | | |
|---|---|---|
| In bulk (e.g. silos, loose on floor) | for long period | 14% or less |
| In bulk | up to one month | 14–16% |
| In sacks | for long period | 16–18% |
| In sacks | a few weeks | 18–20% |

Only fully ripe grain in a very dry period is likely to be harvested in this country at 14% moisture. In a wet season, the moisture content may be over 30% and the grain may have to be dried in two or three stages if a continuous-flow drier is used.

Damp grains, above the limits set out above, will heat and may become useless. This heating is mainly due to the growth of moulds and respiration of the grain. Moulds, beetles and weevils may damage grain which is stored at a high temperature, e.g. grain not cooled properly after drying; or grain from the combine on a very hot day. Ideally, the grain should be cooled to 18°C (65°F)—this is difficult or impossible in hot weather.

Heating and destruction of dry grain in store several months after harvest may be caused by grain weevils and beetles. Insecticides can be used to fumigate silos and grain stores before harvest or applied to the grain when it is being stored. Special formulations of the insecticide *malathion* are commonly used for this purpose.

A recent development is the storage of damp grain, straight from the combine, in sealed silos. Fungi, grain respiration and insects use up the oxygen in the air spaces and give out carbon dioxide and the activity ceases when the oxygen is used up. The grain dies but the feeding value does not deteriorate whilst it remains in the silo. This method is best for damp grain of 18–24% moisture, but grain up to 30% or more may also be stored in this way although it is more likely to cause trouble when removing it from the silo, e.g. "bridging" above an auger. The damp grain is taken out of the silo as required for feeding. This method cannot be used for seed corn, malting barley, or wheat for flour milling.

Another recent development is the storage of damp grain by cooling it. Chilled air is blown through the grain and the higher the moisture content of the grain the lower the temperature must be, e.g.,

| Moisture content of grain | 18% | 20% | 22% |
|---|---|---|---|
| Temperature of grain (approx.) | 7°C (45°F) | 4½°C (40°F) | 2°C (35°F) |

This method is cheaper than drying and the grain stores well, i.e. the germination is not affected and mould growth does not develop and so it can be used for seed, malting or milling. Because the moisture content is higher than in dried grain it is very suitable for rolling for cattle food.

The latest method of storing damp grain safely and economically is by sterilizing it with a slightly volatile acid such as *propionic acid*. The acid is sprayed onto the grain from a special applicator as it passes into the auger conveying it to the storage heap. 5–9 litres/ tonne (1–2 gal/ton) of acid is required. Grain stored in this way is not suitable for milling for human consumption or for seed but it is very satisfactory for animal feeding and after rolling or crushing it remains in a fresh condition for a long time because the acid continues to have a preservative effect.

*Grain quality in cereals.* Good quality grain is dry, clean, plump and has a thin skin or husk; it has been harvested in good conditions and is not musty, discoloured or overheated. If the grain is to be used for seed or malting (barley), the germination must be over 90% (preferably over 95%). A low nitrogen and high starch content is desirable in malting barley grains—high nitrogen grains are better for feeding. Wheat for bread-making should have a high gluten content.

Under E.E.C. regulations, when cereal prices are low, subsidies will be paid for denaturing wheat and for buying wheat and barley at intervention prices. To qualify for these payments the grain must be of a minimum quality standard. The object in denaturing wheat is to prevent the treated grain being used later for human consumption. The process is carried out by licensed denaturers in one of several ways so that the grain is either (a) coloured with a blue dye, (b) mixed with fish oil, or (c) put into an animal feeding-stuff mixture. To qualify for the denaturing subsidy the wheat grain must not have been previously treated and must be as follows:

(1) Free from objectionable odours.

(2) Have a specific weight of not less than 68 kg/hl (54·4 lb/ bushel).

(3) Have a moisture content not above 18%.

(4) Contain less than:
     (a) 15% sprouted grains ⎫
     (b) 3% other cereals   ⎬ maximum 17%.
     (c) 3% other impurities ⎭

For intervention buying, the "standard quality" for wheat and barley means that the grain must be of a sound and fair marketing quality, free from abnormal smell and live pests, and a proper colour, and must have the following: Moisture content 16%; specific weight: wheat 75 kg/hl (68 lb/bushel), barley 67 kg/hl (53·6 lb/bushel); other matter—not more than wheat 5%, barley

4%, including maximum of

| | |
|---|---|
| sprouted grains | 1% |
| broken grains | wheat only 2% |
| grain impurities | wheat 1·5% barley 2% |
| miscellaneous impurities | wheat 0·5% barley 1% |

Special riddle sizes are specified for testing samples of grain. These quality standards may be changed from time to time (further details are contained in the Intervention Board Regulations).

*Cereal straw* is a problem on many farms: it can be baled for use as litter (of decreasing importance now as more stock are kept in cubicles), for feeding (low quality bulk food), and for industrial uses such as paper-making. Straw can be a useful source of humus if it is chopped and/or spread and mixed into the soil as soon as possible after harvest. Burning is the simplest and cheapest method for disposal of straw and helps to control some diseases such as leaf blotch and eyespot, but it is often carelessly done and damage is caused to other crops, hedges, trees, buildings and wild life; the N.F.U. Code of Practice for straw-burning should be strictly followed.

*Varieties.* There are dozens of cereal varieties now on the market and new ones are introduced every year. However, there are only a few outstanding varieties of each cereal and these are described in the annual *Recommended Lists* from the National Institute of Agricultural Botany (N.I.A.B.) for England and Wales, and from the Agricultural Colleges in Scotland and the Ministry of Agriculture for Northern Ireland.

*Seed-dressing.* Cereal seed should be dressed with organo-mercurial seed-dressings to control fungous diseases such as covered *smuts* and *leaf-stripe*. A combined dressing, including insecticides, is useful for controlling *wireworms* and *wheat bulb fly* (see Table 21).

*Fertilizers.* These are usually combine-drilled with the seed, although the star-wheel mechanism used on most drills gives a very uneven distribution of fertilizer. A recent trend is to broadcast the fertilizer and use narrow row widths (100 mm or 4 in.) when sowing the seed; this reduces the labour costs and gives good results on fertile soils. All the fertilizer could be applied in the seed-bed with spring crops. With winter crops most of the nitrogen is top-dressed in the spring.

Average fertilizer requirements:

Phosphate ($P_2O_5$)  40–60 kg/ha (30–50 units/acre)
Potash ($K_2O$) 40–60 kg/ha (30–50 units/acre)
Nitrogen (N) Autumn 0–25 kg/ha (0–20 units/acre)
    Spring—in dry, arable areas 75–100 kg/ha (60–80 units/acre)
    Spring—high rainfall and very fertile areas 25–60 kg/ha (20–50 units/acre).

### WHEAT

*Wheat grain* is used mainly for making *flour*. The type of flour produced varies with different varieties and the growing conditions. Most of the flour is used for making *biscuits* or *cakes* or for *blending* with bread-quality flour from North American wheats. The poorer quality grain and the by-products from white flour production, i.e. *bran* (skin of grain), and various inseparable mixtures of bran and flour (e.g. *weatings*) are fed to pigs, poultry and other stock. Some breakfast foods are made from wheat.

Wheat straw is used mainly for bedding but sometimes for thatching and covering potato clamps (pits).

| Yield | Average | Good |
|---|---|---|
| Grain | 4 tonne/ha (32 cwt/acre) | 6 tonne/ha (48 cwt/acre) |
| Straw | 3 tonne/ha (24 cwt/acre) | 4 tonne/ha (32 cwt/acre) |

*Soils and climate* (pH should be higher than 5·5). Wheat is a deep-rooted plant which grows well on rich and heavy soils and in the sunnier eastern and southern parts of this country. Winter wheat can withstand most of the frosty conditions of this country but is easily killed by water-logged soil conditions.

*Place in rotation.* Wheat is the best cereal to grow when the soil is in a high state of fertility because it is the most resistant to "lodging" and yields best, e.g. it may be taken for 1 or 2 years after grassland and after potatoes. Winter wheat should not be grown continuously for many years because of likely failures due to fungous diseases such as take-all and eye-spot.

*Seed-beds.* A fairly rough autumn seed-bed prevents "soil-capping" in a mild, wet winter and protects the base of the plants from cold frosty winds. In a difficult autumn, winter wheat may be successfully planted in a wet sticky seed-bed and usually produces a good crop. Spring wheat should only be planted in a good seed-bed.

*Time of sowing*

Winter wheat: late September-early February (October best).
Spring wheat: February-early May (March best).

*Methods of sowing*—depth should be about 30-50 mm (1-2 in.)

(1) Drilling (a) combine drill 150-180 mm (6-7 in.) rows
           (b) ordinary drill 100-180 mm (4-7 in.) rows
(2) Broadcasting, e.g. by hand, fiddle, aeroplane, fertilizer spinner.

*Seed-rate:* Winter wheat 125-190 kg/ha (1-1½ cwt/acre)
          Spring wheat 150-220 kg/ha (1¼-1¾ cwt/acre)

*Varieties of wheat.* Winter wheats usually yield better than spring varieties. Most of the modern varieties have red (brown) grain; the white (cream) grained varieties sprout too readily in a damp season. Most winter wheats must pass through a period of low temperatures and short days if they are to yield well—hence they should only be sown in the spring in exceptional circumstances (see N.I.A.B. list).

*Recommended varieties:*

|  | Winter | Spring |
|---|---|---|
| Good quality milling and bread | *Maris Widgeon, Flinor, West Desprez, Maris Freeman* | *Sirius, Sappo* |
| Biscuit quality | *Maris Nimrod, Maris Ranger, Val* | *Maris Butler* |
| Others | *Maris Huntsman, Champlein, Bouquet, Cappelle-Desprez, Mega, Atou* | *Maris Dove, Kleibor, Kolibri* |

See also N.I.A.B. recommended list

Breeding work is now going on in this country to improve yields of wheat by producing dwarf types and special hybrids which are suitable for British conditions; types having nodular nitrogen-fixing bacteria (like legumes) may be produced by modern plant breeding methods—in the distant future.

| | N | | $P_2O_5$ | | $K_2O$ | |
|---|---|---|---|---|---|---|
| | kg/ha | units/ acre | kg/ha | units/ acre | kg/ha | units/ acre |
| Winter wheat in seed-bed | 0– 25 | 0– 20 | 40–60 | 30–50 | 40–60 | 30–50 |
| Spring top-dressing | 50–125 | 40–100 | — | — | — | — |
| Spring wheat | 50–100 | 40– 80 | 40–50 | 30–40 | 40–50 | 30–40 |
| If 25 t/ha (10 tons/acre) of FYM applied | 25– 40 | 20– 30 | — | — | — | — |

The lower figures for nitrogen shown in the table above would be adequate if the wheat was taken after grassland containing clovers or lucerne.

*Spring grazing of winter wheat*. If the crop is well forward in the spring and the soil is dry, it can provide useful grazing for sheep or cattle about late March. It should only be grazed once and should be top-dressed with nitrogen afterwards unless the reason for grazing was to reduce the risk of lodging.

*Harvesting*. Winter wheat ripens before spring wheat; the crop is harvested in August and September. Indications of ripeness for harvesting:

(a) *Binder*    Straw: yellowish, all greenness gone.

Grain: in cheesy condition, firm but not hard.

(b) *Combine* (7–10 days later) Straw: turning whitish; nodes shrivelled.

Grain: easily rubbed from ears, hard and dry.

*Tillering of wheat* (and other cereals). The production of side shoots (i.e. tillering) is a very important characteristic of cereals. Where the plants are thinly spaced more side shoots are likely to be produced than where they are close together and so a crop which is uneven in the seedling stage can even up considerably before harvest. All side shoots do not produce ears.

*Lodging in wheat* (and other cereals). Lodging (laying flat) is usually caused by wind and rain. It is most likely to occur when:

(a) the field is in an exposed situation,

(b) the variety is weak-strawed,

(c) excessive amounts of nitrogen are present in the soil, resulting in long weak straw and delayed ripening—this is likely to occur after a clovery ley or where too much nitrogen-fertilizer has been applied. A wet season makes matters worse,

(d) the straw is elongated and weakened due to shading when the plants are too dense or shaded by trees,

(e) the crop is attacked by the eye-spot fungus or foot-rot.

If the crop lodges when the straw is still green and growing the stems can bend at the nodes and grow upright again.

Lodging near maturity may not affect yield provided the pick-up reel mechanism on the combine is set properly when harvesting. It does, however, increase the cost of harvesting and grain quality may be spoiled.

A chemical spray—chlormequat (C.C.C., "cycocel")—can be used on wheat crops, and less effectively, on oat crops to reduce the risk of lodging and consequent loss of yield. It is applied at the five-leaf to "jointing" stages of growth; this results in shorter, stronger, straw (shorter internodes and thick walls) and allows optimum rates of nitrogen to be applied with little risk of lodging. Chlormequat may be mixed with most weed-killer sprays if the timing of application is not too late for weed control. The thicker straw enables treated crops to withstand attacks of eyespot better, but the shorter, denser crops are often attacked earlier by leaf diseases such as Yellow rust.

Barley is a very important arable crop at the present time. The grain is used mainly for *feeding* to all classes of stock—especially pigs, dairy cows and intensively fed beef, and also for *malting* (about 20%).

The best quality grain (see p. 128) is usually sold for *malting*. In this process the wetted grain is sprouted, dried, and the *malt* produced is used for brewing beer, ale and stout, distilling whisky, or producing malt vinegar. Barley *straw* is usually used for bedding; some is fed to cattle.

| *Yield* | Average | Good |
|---|---|---|
| Grain | 3·5 tonne/ha (28 cwt/acre) | 5 tonnes/ha (40 cwt/acre) |
| Straw | 3 tonne/ha (24 cwt/acre) | 4·5 tonnes/ha (36 cwt/acre) |

*Soils and climate* (pH should be about 6·5). Barley is a shallow-rooted crop which grows very well on chalk and limestone soils. It also does well on other types of soil provided they are well limed and drainage is good. On rich and heavy soils barley is likely to "lodge"—especially in a wet season—and the quality of the grain is unlikely to be suitable for malting.

*Place in rotation.* Usually taken at a stage where fertility is not high. Many farmers are now successfully growing spring barley continuously on the same fields.

*Seed-beds.* Winter barley should be planted in a fairly fine seed-bed with some lumps left on the surface. Spring barley needs a fine, uniform seed-bed; loose in top 50 mm (2 in.) and firm underneath.

*Time and methods of sowing:* similar to wheat.

*Seed rate:* 150 kg/ha (1¼ cwt/acre)–180 kg/ha (1½ cwt) for late sowings and in poor seed-beds; 125 kg/ha (1 cwt) for feeding barley in good seed-beds.

*Varieties.* Spring barleys usually yield better and have better quality grain than winter barley. The main advantage of winter barley is that it ripens very early (usually in July).

*Popular varieties:*

|  | Winter | Spring |
|---|---|---|
| Malting quality | *Maris Otter* | *Mazurka, Wing, Berac, Hassan, Zephyr, Gerka, Imber, Proctor, Maris Mink, Golden Promise* |
| Feeding quality | *Astrix, Mirra, Senta* | *Lofa Abed, Julia, Vada, Midas, Abacus, Armelle, Universe* |
| Cyst eelworm resistant |  | *Sabarlis* |

See also N.I.A.B. recommended list

*Fertilizers.* General requirements are similar to wheat except that the amount of nitrogen applied in spring to winter barley should be 50–70 kg/ha (40–60 units) and to malting barley 25–60 kg/ha (20–50 units). Up to 125 kg/ha (100 units) of nitrogen are required for continuous barley crops. F.Y.M. is seldom applied before planting barley.

*Spring grazing of winter barley.* It can be grazed like winter wheat but this is seldom done.

*Harvesting*

Winter barley ready July–early August.

Spring barley ready August–early September.

Barley is ready for harvesting by binder or combine when the straw has turned whitish and the ears are hanging downwards parallel to the straw. In a crop containing late tillers, harvesting should start when most of the crop is ready. Possible malting crops should be left to become as dead ripe as possible before harvesting. Harvesting of feeding barley is often started before the ideal stage— especially if a large acreage has to be harvested and the weather is uncertain. The ears of over-ripe crops and some varieties break off easily; this can result in serious losses.

The pick-up reel now fitted to most combines is very useful for picking up laid crops.

OATS

Oats are mainly used for feeding to livestock—they are particularly good for horses and are also valuable for cattle and sheep but are not very suitable for pigs because of their high husk (fibre) content. The best quality oats may be sold for making oatmeal which is used for breadmaking, oatcakes, porridge, breakfast foods and for feeding chickens.

Barley has largely replaced oats in cattle rations in recent years and the area in oats has been declining for many years. Recently there has been some renewed interest in the crop as a possible "break" from continuous barley because oats are resistant to several of the diseases which affect barley—especially eyespot and some types of take-all. There is also a renewed interest in the "naked" oats species which has a very high feeding value (better than maize) because the husk threshes off the grain. The varieties of this species are very low yielding for various reasons such as being more susceptible to disease, lodging and shedding before harvest. A new, higher yielding variety (Nuprime) has been bred in France and breeding work has now started in this country to produce better varieties for grain production for possible replacement of imported maize.

Oat straw is very variable in quality. The best quality from leafy varieties is similar in feeding value to medium quality hay. Some short, stiff-strawed varieties are no better than barley straw when grown in the warmer, drier parts of this country.

| Yield | Average | Good |
|---|---|---|
| Grain | 3 tonne/ha (24 cwt/acre) | 4·5 tonne/ha (36 cwt/acre) |
| Straw | 2·5 tonne/ha (1–2 ton/acre) | 5 tonne/ha (2 ton/acre) |

*Soils and climate.* pH should be about 5 or over—if too much lime is present, manganese deficiency (grey-leaf) may reduce yields.

Oats do best in the cooler and wetter northern and western parts of this country, but even in these areas they have been replaced by barley on many farms. They will grow on most types of soil and can withstand moderately acid conditions where wheat and barley would fail.

*Place in rotation.* Oats can be taken at almost any stage in a rotation of crops. If grown too often cyst eelworms may cause a crop failure.

*Seed-bed* and *methods of sowing:* similar to wheat.

*Time of sowing: winter oats,* late September–October; *spring,* February–March.

*Seed rate:* 190–250 kg/ha (1½–2 cwt/acre).

*Varieties.* Winter varieties are not so frost hardy as winter wheat or barley; they usually yield better—especially in the drier districts—and are less likely to be damaged by *frit fly* than spring oats.

*Popular varieties:*

Winter: *Maris Osprey, Pendrwm, Peniarth, Maris Quest.*

Spring: Mainly grain. *Leanda, Mostyn, Selma, Astor, Maris Tabard.*

Grain and straw. *Karin, Ayr Commando, Maelor.*

Cyst eelworm resistant. *Nelson.*

(See also recommended lists.)

*Fertilizers:* similar to wheat, but less nitrogen.

| N. 50–60 kg/ha | $P_2O_5$ 40–50 kg/ha | $K_2O$ 40–50 kg/ha |
|---|---|---|
| (40–50 units/acre) | (30–40 units/acre) | (30–40 units/acre) |

*Spring grazing:* that similar to wheat may be desirable if there is a risk of lodging because the grazing results in shorter straw.

*Harvesting.* There is still a high proportion of the oat crop cut with the binder—usually when the straw is still green or just turning yellow; this early cutting gives better quality straw and there is less shedding of grain.

If combined, the crop must be left until it is fully ripe; there is then a serious risk of shedding by high winds or if bad weather holds up the work. Swathing reduces this risk.

### RYE

Rye is grown on a small scale in this country for grain or very early grazing. The grain is used mainly for making rye crispbread; it is not in demand for feeding to livestock.

The long, tough straw is very good for thatching and bedding but is no good for feeding.

|        | Average                    | Good                       |
|--------|----------------------------|----------------------------|
| Grain  | 2·5 t/ha (20 cwt/acre)     | 3·75 t/ha (30 cwt/acre)    |
| Straw  | 3·75 t/ha (30 cwt/acre)    | 5·0 t/ha (40 cwt/acre)     |

*Soils and climate.* Rye will grow on poor, light acid soils and in dry districts where other cereals would fail. It is mainly grown in such conditions for grain because, on good soils, although the yields may be higher, it does not yield or sell so well as other cereals.

Rye is extremely frost hardy and will withstand much colder conditions than the other cereals.

*Place in rotation.* Rye can replace cereals in a rotation—especially where the fertility is not too high. It can be grown continuously on poor soils with occasional breaks of carrots, sugar-beet or leys. Grazing rye is usually taken as a catch crop before kale or roots.

*Seed-beds and methods of sowing:* similar to wheat.

*Time of sowing: winter,* September–October; *spring,* February–March. Grazing rye should, if possible, be sown in late August or early September.

*Seed rate:* for grain, 190 kg/ha (1½ cwt/acre). Early sowing for grazing 125 kg/ha (1 cwt/acre).

*Varieties.* Most of the rye varieties grown now are winter types. Rye, unlike the other cereals, is cross-fertilized so varieties are difficult to maintain true to type and new seed should be bought in each year.

*Popular varieties*

Winter (grain): *King II, Petkus, Dominant.*
Grazing: *Lovaszpatonai, Ovari, Rheidol.*

*Fertilizers.* On light soils, for grain.

| N 50–60 kg/ha      | $P_2O_5$ 40–50 kg/ha   | $K_2O$ 40–50 kg/ha     |
|--------------------|------------------------|------------------------|
| (40–50 units/acre) | (30–50 units/acre)     | (30–40 units/acre)     |

Same amounts used for grazing rye on better soils. The nitrogen is normally applied as a top-dressing in February.

*Spring grazing.* The special varieties for early spring grazing (late February–March) can be grazed at least twice if the grazing is started before the plants develop hollow stems. Once-grazed crops can be left to harvest as grain which is usually sold for seed.

*Harvesting.* Rye is normally the first of the cereal crops to ripen. It is cut with the binder or combine near the dead ripe stage when the grain is hard and dry and the straw turning from a greyish to whitish appearance. The ears sprout very readily in a wet harvest season. If the crop is grown for its high quality straw it should be cut with the binder before the grain develops and so the straw is not damaged by threshing.

### MIXED CORN CROPS

Mixtures of cereals (*dredge corn*) are grown in some areas—particularly in the south-west. The commonest type is a mixture of barley and oats in various proportions with a total seed rate of about 220 kg/ha (1¾ cwt/acre). The yield of grain is usually better than if either crop was grown alone. Varieties must be chosen which ripen at the same time.

Sometimes cereals and peas or beans are mixed (*mashlum*)—this type can be used for silage or grain.

Winter and spring mixtures are used.

*Growing and harvesting:* grain—similar to oats, silage—forage harvester.

### MAIZE

Maize was introduced into this country about 200 years ago as a forage crop, but never really became established until recently with the introduction of much more suitable varieties, improved cultural and harvesting methods, and much enthusiasm.

It is a tall annual grass plant with a strong, solid stem carrying large narrow leaves. The male flowers are produced on a tassel at the top of the plant and the female some distance away on one or more spikes in the axils of the leaves. (This separation simplifies the production of hybrid seed.) After wind pollination of the filament-like styles (silks) the grain develops in rows on the female spike (cob) to produce the maize ear in its surrounding husk leaves.

The main uses for the crop in this country are for making *silage* (cut when the grain on the cob is still soft or cheesy) or for harvesting as ripened grain; some is grazed or cut and fed as a forage crop, and there is a limited, but profitable, market for "corn-on-the-cob" or sweet corn as a vegetable—this latter is a special type of maize in which some of the sugar produced is not converted into starch and is harvested when the grain is in the milky stage.

*Climatic requirements.* Maize growing in Britain is limited, because it will not grow until the temperature is above 10°C (50°F)—most other crops and weeds start growth at 4–5°C. Good yields are very much dependent on plenty of sunshine. Exposed (windy) situations are not suitable. Maize for grain can only be grown successfully in lowland areas (below 400 ft) in the south-eastern counties; for silage, the area can be extended to sheltered parts of the midland and south-western counties. Wet autumns make grain harvesting very difficult.

*Suitable soils.* Ideally, a rich, deep, well-drained loam is best. Light soils are reasonable if they do not dry out. Thin chalk soils should be avoided and heavy soils are usually very slow to warm up in spring. A soil pH of 6·0 or over is desirable.

*Place in rotation.* Maize can be grown on the same field for many years, but it is usually grown as a cereal break-crop because it is resistant to cereal cyst eelworm, take-all, eyespot, and the foliar diseases which attack wheat and barley. It might also be used as a cleaning drop, as it is planted late, after the spring flush of wild oat growth, and the herbicide atrazine can be used to destroy couch and other weeds.

*Seedbed.* The seed should be planted about 50 mm (2 in.) deep in a level, moist, friable seedbed. This can usually be produced by good ploughing, up to 250 mm (10 in.) deep, in autumn, leaving a fairly level surface for frost action and avoiding deep working in spring which might produce a cloddy tilth. Soil pans should be broken up by subsoiling.

*Manuring.* Yields can be improved by applying F.Y.M. or slurry, if available.

Nitrogen—up to 100 kg/ha (125 units/acre) applied in seedbed.

Phosphate and Potash—about 60 kg/ha (50 units/acre) of each ploughed in during the autumn, plus an extra 50–06 kg/ha (40–50 units/acre) in the seedbed where one or both nutrients are deficient.

*Sowing.* Maize should be drilled at the end of April or early May with a precision drill fitted with the correct belt, cell wheel or plate to ensure an even and correct distribution of undamaged seed. A row width of 750 mm (30 in.) is satisfactory for most conditions. A 20-row headland should be used to facilitate harvesting.

*Plant populations:*

|  | Grain | Silage |
|---|---|---|
| Plants per acre | 35,000 | 45,000 |
| Plants per hectare | 90,000 | 110,000 |
| Distance between plants in 750 mm rows | 150 mm | 110 mm |
| Seed rates in kg/ha or lb/acre | 24–30 | 30–40 |

*Varieties.* Most of the hybrid varieties grown in Britain are Flint × Dent crosses. Some examples of these are:

|  | Grain | Silage | Sweet corn |
|---|---|---|---|
| Early | Dekalb 202 Pioneer 131 | LG 11 Austria 290 | Early King Indian Dawn |
| Late | Anjou 196 | Inra 321 | October Gold |

*Pests and diseases.* Seedling blight—use thiram seed dressing.

Foot-rot or stalk-rot—choose resistant varieties.

Frit fly and wireworm—use phorate granules in seedbed.

Leatherjackets and wireworm—use gamma BHC.

Birds (rooks, pigeons and pheasants) can cause very serious damage at the emergence stage—especially on small areas; various controls can be used such as dawn and dusk patrols, bangers, dead cats, and black nylon thread about waist height between canes or sticks at 10–40 metre spacings.

*Weed control.* Weeds can ruin a maize crop because of their faster growth rate in May and June. However, most annual broad-leaved weeds and blackgrass can be controlled by the herbicide atrazine applied at planting time; much heavier doses applied in two stages (half worked into seedbed in early spring and half at planting will kill couch grass, but because of residues a second crop of maize must follow). Couch also controlled by EPTC *plus* antidote.

*Harvesting.* (a) For silage—usually about the end of September. The crop is cut and chopped into small pieces (10–15 mm) with a special chopper or a forage harvester with a maize attachment when the grain is in the cheesy state; it can be stored in bunker or tower silos. The dry matter can vary from 25% or more with some early varieties to 20% with late varieties, and dry matter yields can be over 10 tonne/ha (5 tons/acre). Additives are not required, but rapid filling and good sealing are important in producing good silage. Urea or ammonia may be added to increase the protein content of the silage. A less fibrous, but much lower yielding, silage can be made by grinding or chopping the ears only, i.e. grain and cob (rachis).

(b) For grain—usually ready between mid-October and mid-November. Frosts will kill off the foliage and this facilitates combining and helps to dry the grain, which in the yellow hard condition has a moisture content of 35–45% at harvest. Various types of machines are available for harvesting—some are ordinary combines with header attachments which only remove the ears from the standing crop and then thresh off the grain; others thresh the whole crop and some deliver the complete or dehusked ears into a trailer to be shelled later.

Drying the grain can be a problem and is very expensive. It usually has to be dried in two or three stages in a continuous drier from 40% to 15% moisture content. Floor-drying cannot be used for threshed grain, but the whole ears can be dried in this way.

Wet storage is possible in air-tight tower or butyl silos, but it can be difficult to unload and deteriorates rapidly when taken out of the silo.

Propionic acid, applied at 18 litres (4 gal)/tonne through a special applicator will preserve the wet grain very satisfactorily in heaps in existing buildings.

Straw-choppers or a rotavator may have to be used to help dispose of the maize trash after harvest.

Yield. Silage (very variable)  25–60 tonne/ha (10–25 ton/acre)

      Grain                 4–6 tonne/ha (30–45 cwt/acre)

      Vegetable cobs     up to 75,000/ha (30,000/acre)

(See also M.A.F.F. leaflet No. 93 and Maize Development Association literature.)

## Pulse Crops

Pulse crops are *legumes* which have edible seeds; the main ones grown in this country are the various types of *beans* and *peas*. Bacteria on the roots of these crops can fix nitrogen, so, normally, they do not require nitrogen fertilizers and the following crop benefits from nitrogen left in the soil about 60 kg/ha (50 units/acre).

Beans and peas are useful, protein-rich grains for blending with cereals for feeding farm stock, but yields may be disappointing and harvesting troublesome. At present, peas are mainly grown for human consumption in the canned, quick-frozen, or dried state; beans for human consumption (canned, frozen and dried) are increasing in importance as a farm crop now that they can be mechanically harvested, e.g. dwarf stringless beans.

The smaller (tick) beans and maple peas are popular for pigeon feeding and high prices are paid for good quality grain.

Beans and peas can be used in mixtures with cereals for ensilage.

Stock-feeding beans usually grow well on heavy soils and loams, whereas peas, French and runner beans prefer the medium and lighter soils.

Beans or peas provide a useful break between cereal crops but should not be grown in successive years because of fungous diseases and pests—although climbing French (kidney) beans are sometimes grown on the same site for several years where fixed support wires have been erected.

The introduction of improved varieties, chemical control of weeds and pests such as aphids, may result in a greater acreage being grown for stock feedings.

BEANS

*Types*

(a) *Stock-feeding (Field beans)*

    (1) *Winter beans.* These are not very frost hardy and are more susceptible to "chocolate spot" disease but usually yield much better and ripen 2–4 weeks earlier than spring beans.

    (2) *Spring beans.* There are two main types—*tick (tic)* beans— small seeds and *horse* beans—large seeds.

(See N.I.A.B. leaflet on *Field Beans*.)

*Yields of grain*

|  | Winter beans | | Spring beans | |
|---|---|---|---|---|
|  | Average | Good | Average | Good |
| t/ha | 3 | 4·25 | 2·5 | 3·75 |
| cwt/acre | 24 | 34 | 20 | 30 |

(b) *Human consumption.* Various types of beans such as broad beans, dwarf (French) types ("green" beans), and navy (baked) beans are increasing in importance as contract farm-scale vegetable crops; they are mechanically harvested for canning, quick-freezing, and drying. Expert advice should be obtained from the processors and other advisers before growing these crops. (See also *M.A.F.F. Bulletin* No. 87, *Beans*.)

*Soils and climate.* Field beans grow well on clay soils and heavy loams provided they are well drained and limed (pH above 6·0–the nodule bacteria work is better when pH is high). Soils rich in organic matter and nitrogen usually produce too much straw and poor yields of grain.

The French and runner beans prefer loams and lighter soils—especially where irrigation is possible.

Winter beans are risky to grow north of the Midlands because of possible frost damage. French beans are easily damaged by frost.

*Seed-bed:* deeper, but otherwise similar to cereals.

*Sowing.* Winter beans do best if sown in early October at about 250 kg/ha (2 cwt/acre). Spring beans should be sown in late February or early March at a similar rate.

Spring beans may be sown in wide rows, 450–600 mm (18–24 in.) apart, so that weeds can be controlled by inter-row cultivations, and the crop is not damaged by tractor wheels when sprayed to control aphids. Winter and spring beans may be sown in narrow rows with the corn drill but care is required to avoid damage to the seed and "bridging" in the drill. The depth of sowing should be 75 mm (3 in.). In difficult conditions the beans may be ploughed in—not more than 100 mm (4 in.) deep—or broad cast on the ploughing and covered by harrows.

*Weed Control (field beans).* Most annual weeds can be controlled by pre-emergence (sometimes post-emergence) treatment of the soil with simazine—the seed must be planted at least 75 mm (3 in.) deep to avoid herbicide damage which takes the form of blackening of the leaf edges and possibly death of the plant. Wild oats can be controlled by tri-allate applied to the seed-bed or barban post emergence. Dinoseb-acetate may be used post-emergence—before the beans are 200 mm (8 in.) high—for control of annual broad-leaved weeds.

*Fertilizers.* 25 tonne/ha (10 tons/acre) of F.Y.M. is beneficial, if available. Also, for good conditions, about 50 kg/ha (40 units/acre) of both $P_2O_5$ and $K_2O$ broadcast or preferably placed in bands about 50 mm (2 in.) from the seed. Green and navy beans also require nitrogen—up to about 120 kg/ha (150 units/acre).

*Treatment during the growing season.* Honey bees, 2 or 3 hives/ha (1/acre), are usually necessary, especially with crops for seed, to help with the pollination of beans. This results in a quick set (fertilization) of the maximum number of pods which each plant can fill, and also, more even ripening, an earlier harvest and better yields. Some new hybrid varieties being developed are self-fertilizing and so are less dependent on bees than the common open-pollinated varieties. Systemic aphicides, which may be required to control black fly (aphid), should, if possible, be applied before flowering (June) to give better control with less risk of damage to the bees. These chemicals, which are normally only required for spring beans, may be applied as sprays (e.g. *menazon*) or granules (e.g. *phorate* or *disulfoton*).

*Harvesting.* Winter beans are usually ready for harvesting in August and spring beans in September or October. They ripen unevenly—the lower pods are first to mature.

The crop is ready for cutting with the binder when the pods about half way up the stem have turned black and the scar (hilum) where the bean is attached to the pod is also black. At this stage there are green pods and leaves on the plant but these will ripen during the 2–4 weeks in the stooks before they are stacked.

Most crops are now harvested by combine when the leaves have withered and nearly all the pods are ripe.

The straw cut early with the binder is reasonably good for feeding; but combined straw is useless.

Some grain is lost by shedding by both methods—sheep will pick up beans from the stubbles.

Binder-harvested beans are seldom threshed before the following January.

*Drying and Storage.* Combined beans may require drying before storage. They should be dried carefully— preferably in two stages— if moisture content is much over 20%. Storage conditions and bushel weight are the same as wheat (64 lb/bushel). See M.A.F.F. leaflet STL No. 60—Field Beans.

PEAS

*Type* 1. *For human consumption (white-flowered)*

(a) Threshed (dry) peas—sold loose, in packets, or canned; marrowfats (e.g. *Maro*); blues (e.g. *Pauli* and *Vedette*).
*Yield:* 2·5–4·0 t/ha (20–32 cwt/acre).

(b) Vining peas—for canning fresh ("garden peas"), quick-freezing or artificial drying.

These are grown under contract and seed is supplied by the purchasing firms—there is a wide range of dwarf varieties including early, medium and late types.
*Yield:* average 4·0 t/ha (32 cwt/acre) good 6 t/ha (48 cwt/acre).

(c) Pulling peas—sold as fresh peas in the pod.

There are many varieties and they are mainly grown as a market garden crop.
*Yield:* average 7·5 t/ha (3 tons/acre) good 11 t/ha (4½ tons/acre).

*Type* 2. *For stock-feeding and pigeons* (reddish flowers), e.g.

Maple peas (brown and yellow mottled grain).
*Yield:* average 2·5 t/ha (1 ton/acre) good 3·5 t/ha (28 cwt/acre).

*Soils and climate.* Peas grow best on loam and lighter types of soil, provided they are well drained and limed (pH well above 5·5). The threshed peas require good harvest weather for drying in the field—less than 50 mm (2 in.) of rain in July and August—and so are only grown in the eastern and some Midland counties. Vining and pulling peas are not so dependent on dry weather at harvest and are grown in most of the arable areas within easy range of a factory or market.

*Seed-bed.* The peas should be drilled about 50 mm (2 in.) deep in a loose tilth. On the lighter soils they may be drilled into well broken furrow slices or after one harrowing.

*Sowing.* Narrow rows (120–180 mm) are common with weeds controlled by herbicides; inter-row weed control by cultivation requires wider rows (250–400 mm), i.e. 10–16 in.

*Seed rate.* Usually about 250 kg/ha (2 cwt/acre) of treated seed (e.g. drazoxolon), but this should be varied according to seed size, germination, quality of seedbed, and time of sowing.

*Fertilizer.* $P_2O_5$ 40 kg/ha (30 units/acre) $K_2O$ 90 kg/ha (70 units/acre) for average conditions ideally "placed" (60 mm from the seed).

*Time of sowing*

*Threshed* peas: early March.

*Vining* peas: February–May, according to the factory fieldsman's instructions (usually based on a "heat units" system).

*Pulling* peas: January–April.

*Weed control.* Most of the troublesome annual weeds, with the possible exception of cleavers, can be controlled by pre-emergence herbicides containing one or more of the following chemicals: *aziprotryne, cyanazine, prometryne, trietazine* and *simazine;* alternatively, *dinoseb* or *cyanazine* can be applied post-emergence, but with the risk of damaging the peas if the wax coating on the leaves is not normal. MCPB is sometimes used to control some perennial broad-leaved weeds, e.g. thistles. Wild oats can be controlled by *propham, tri-allate* or TCA applied in the seedbed or *barban* at early seedling stage.

Light harrowing (on a dry day) in the early stages of growth (2–4 in.) will kill some annual weed seedlings.

*Harvesting.* Peas are usually cut with special pea-cutters or mowers fitted with special lifters. The crop is left in windrows.

*Threshed* and stock-feed peas are ready when the vines and pods have turned a yellow or light brown colour and before the seed starts to shed. After partly drying on the ground the crop can be put on tripods, 4-poles, or racks to complete drying. Alternatively, it may be desiccated by spraying with diquat and combined direct 1–2 weeks later. If drying is necessary it must be done slowly and at a low temperature 43°C (110°F). The storage moisture content is the same as for cereals.

*Vining* peas are cut when the crop is still green and just starting to lose colour. The haulms (and pods) are put through a special vining machine which separates the peas from the pods. These machines were originally at fixed sites and the whole crop had to be carted to them; nowadays most crops are harvested by large mobile viners which can work 24 hours a day in all weathers, and they normally pick up the crop from windrows left by special pea-cutters. The shelled peas are then rushed to the factory for canning, freezing or drying. The haulms (vines) may be made into silage or hay, or worked into the soil to provide organic matter.

*Pulling peas* are harvested by removing the pods when the peas are in a fresh, sweet condition; this requires a large gang of casual labour or very expensive machinery and so the acreage grown is rapidly declining. (See also *M.A.F.F. Bulletin* No. 81, *Peas.* also Vol. 1, *Pea and Bean Growers Handbook* from P.G.R.O)

### Linseed and Flax

These are varieties of the same plant; *linseed* is grown for seed for oil extraction and cattle cake, *flax* is grown for the fibres in the stems which are used for making linen.

Flax is not grown in this country now and linseed is only grown on a very small scale as a cereal break-crop.

### Oil-seed Rape

This crop is grown for the oil, extracted from its small black seed, and used for the manufacture of margarine, cooking-fats, and specialized lubricants for jet engines. It has become increasingly popular under E.E.C. conditions because of the increasing demand for the crop and the very high prices being paid for it. It will grow in a wide range of soil and climatic conditions provided the soil is well drained and pH is over 6·0. It is a very useful break-crop for cereals, and the cereal machinery can be used for growing and harvesting it.

*Winter* types are more popular on the continent; they are sown in August or early September and harvested the following July or August and usually yield better than the spring types. Varieties: *Major, Victor, Rapol.*

*Spring* types are more popular in this country mainly because of the severe damage which can be caused by pigeons feeding on over-wintering crops: also stubble cleaning can be done in the autumn. Usually sown late March or early April and harvested in late August or early September. Varieties: *Gulle, Zephyr, Oro.*

*Rotation.* Ideally about one year in four.

*Seedbed.* The small seed requires a fine, firm seedbed.

*Seed rate.* 6–10 kg/ha (lb/acre); it may have to be mixed with fertilizer or other material for sowing with most types of corn drill. Row width may be narrow 125–175 mm (5–7 in.) or wide 450 mm (18 in.) to allow for inter-row cultivations.

*Fertilizers*

|            | N       | $P_2O_5$ | $K_2O$  |
|------------|---------|----------|---------|
| kg/ha      | 75–190  | 40–50    | 40–100  |
| units/acre | 60–150  | 30–40    | 30–80   |

Most of the nitrogen for winter rape is applied in the spring.

*Weed control.* A good crop of oil-seed rape will smother most broad-leaved weeds—but not grass weeds; in fact, spring rape can be under-sown with grasses being established for seed production. Herbicides such as *propachlor, alachlor* and *nitrofen* can be used to control many broad-leaved annual weeds, but will not control brassica weeds such as charlock, runch and mustard: the latter is a problem because crops containing it are likely to be rejected. Couch should be controlled before planting. Chickweed must be controlled.

Wild oats: use *TCA, di-allate,* or *barban.*

Self-sown cereals (in winter rape): use *dalapon* in the autumn

*Carbetamide* (new) controls cereals, grasses and other weeds.

*Pest control*—likely to become more troublesome as more crops are grown. Flea beetles—controlled by BHC seed dressing. Pollen beetles and seed weevils—controlled by BHC, malathion.

*Harvesting* (two methods may be used):

(a) Direct combining—this is done when most of the seed is hard and black; because of unevenness in ripening there will be some losses due to shedding and some unripe seed. Only a few days are available for harvesting at the right time. Desiccation with diquat before harvest eases the work on direct combining.

(b) Windrowing—this is done with a special windrowing machine or modified pea-cutter, and allows more time for the combining operation; the crop is cut when the seed is reddish-brown in colour and left on a 6–9 in. stubble in a swath (windrow) for 10–14 days and then picked up by the combine. Careful setting of the combine is very important; care must be taken to avoid losses of the very small seed through holes in elevators, trailers, etc.

*Drying.* The seed must be dried to 9% moisture content for storage and sale; this must be done as soon as possible because damp seed rapidly deteriorates.

*Yield.* 1·8—3·1 tonne/ha (15–25 cwt/acre).

Oil content about 40–42%.

See M.A.F.F. leaflet STL No. 76.)

### Potatoes

*Uses.* Potatoes are mainly used for human consumption—about 86 kg (190 lb) per head are eaten every year as boiled or baked potatoes, chips, crisps, etc. An increasing proportion of the crop (nearly 20%) is processed as crisps, frozen chips, dehydrated instant mash and canned "new" potatoes.

Good quality ware potato tubers

(a) are not damaged or diseased,

(b) are free of greening, second growth irregularities and sprouts,

(c) have smooth clean skins which are easily peeled,

(d) have flesh which does not blacken,

(e) are of reasonable size and shape.

Tubers for crisps, chips and dehydration should have a high dry-matter (starch) content and a low sugar content (too much sugar produces dark brown crisps and chips). For canning, waxy tubers of low dry matter are preferred and in the size range 20–30 mm ($\frac{3}{4}$ to $1\frac{1}{4}$ in.). 8–10 oz. tubers are popular for baking.

*Varieties* (see N.I.A.B. recommended list).

*Popular varieties*

Fresh potatoes—Earlies, *Maris Peer, Homeguard, Red Craigs Royal, Ulster Prince, Maris Page, Arran Pilot.*

　　　　　Maincrop, *Pentland Crown, King Edward, Pentland Dell, Maris Piper, Desiree, Majestic, Pentland Ivory, Stormont Enterprise.*

Processing—Crisps, *Record, Homeguard, Bintje, Golden Wonder.*

　　　　Chips, *Pentland Crown, Pentland Dell, Majestic.*

　　　　Dehydration, *King Edward, Redskin, Red Craigs Royal.*

　　　　Canning, *Arran Pilot, Maris Peer, King Edward, Pentland Marble.*

| | Yield of tubers | | Seed rate | | Time of planting | Time of harvesting |
|---|---|---|---|---|---|---|
| | t/ha | tons/ acre | t-ha | cwt/ acre | | |
| Earlies | 10–30 | 4–12 | 3–5 | 24–40 | Feb.–March | June–July |
| Maincrop | 25–50 | 10–20 | 2–2.5 | 16–20 | April | Sept.–Oct. |
| Seed | 20–30 | 8–12 | 3–4 | 24–32 | April | Sept.–Oct. |
| Canning | 10–20 | 4–8 | 5.0–7.5 | 40–60 | March–June | June–Oct. |

The seed-rates shown above are suitable when normal seed-sized tubers are used, i.e. 30–60 mm ($1\frac{1}{4}$–$2\frac{1}{4}$ in.). If small seed is used (20–30 mm) the seed rate can be reduced by about 25%.

*Suitable soils.* Main crops grow best on deep loam soils. Earlies do best on early light soils in areas free from late frosts.

*Place in rotation.* This may be taken at any stage but maincrops or seed should not be grown more often than two years in eight because root eelworms may build up in the soil.

*Seed-bed preparation.* Early, deep ploughing is necessary to allow for frost action. Deep cultivation, harrowing, and, if necessary, rotary cultivation are required to produce a fine deep tilth without losing too much moisture.

On silty clay soils the "Dutch" method of planting may be followed. The aim is to build up ridges of clod-free soil over the tubers so that mechanical harvesting is facilitated. Autumn cultivations consist of subsoiling, if necessary, to break soil pans—this should only be done when the soil is reasonably dry and a good cracking effect is possible. Ploughing should be fast, not more than 200–250 mm (8–10 in.) deep and furrow slices about 250 mm wide. In spring the soil should be shallow worked 50–70 mm (2–3 in.) deep and then low ridges made to just cover the tubers. Further inter-row workings over several weeks are aimed at building up the ridge with fine soil.

*Seed potatoes.* The "seed" which the farmer plants is a tuber, not a true seed. This is a vegetative method of reproduction and all healthy plants of the same variety are alike. New varieties are produced by sowing the true seeds found in the green tomato-like fruits which develop from the flowers of some varieties.

The best quality "seed" potatoes are produced in Scotland, the northern parts of Ireland and the high areas of England and Wales because the greenflies (aphids) which spread virus diseases are not common in these areas. In lowland areas, where aphids are common, some control of them (and disease spread) can be obtained by using systemic insecticides, when farmers wish to grow their own "seed" instead of buying in new "seed" every year. Only certified seed can be sold for planting; the main classifications of certified seed are: VTSC (Virus Tested from Stem Cuttings); FS (Foundation Seed); class AA (commercial seed grade); and grade CC which can only be used for ware potato production (see also page 178).

*Sprouting of tubers before planting.* This is necessary with earlies and desirable for main crops and seed crops. The tubers are placed in special sprouting boxes which allow light to reach them. The boxed seed is stored during the winter in glasshouses which can be heated to prevent frost damage or in sheds fitted with warm–white fluorescent tube lighting. The rate of growth of the sprouts is increased by raising the temperature; the size of the sprout is controlled by light—short, sturdy sprouts are formed in well-lighted sheds. The main advantages are: earlier growth, less risk of blight, higher yields, earlier harvesting, and rogues can be removed from seed crops because they have different sprouts.

Tubers to be used for seed production and for producing canning size potatoes should be sprouted late—this results in more sprouts per tuber and so more small size tubers in the harvested crop. Tubers sprouted early usually produce only one sprout per tuber—this is desirable for earlies to give the crop a quick start. The increasing use of automatic planters means that more attention must be paid to the size of the sprouts at time of planting—ideally they should not be more than 6 mm ($\frac{1}{4}$ in.) long and this can be achieved by keeping the seed tubers at 4°–5°C until about 3 weeks before planting time when the temperature should be raised to 10°–15°C—so producing "mini" sprouts.

If the tubers are planted by hand or placed by hand in cups on mechanical planters, the sprouts can be larger 25–35 mm (1–1$\frac{1}{2}$ in.).

The temperature range for sprouting is 5°C (41°F)–18°C (65°F).

For fuller details on sprouting see M.A.F.F. advisory leaflet No. 504

*Planting.* This is done either by:

(a) mechanical planters (2–7 row) which may be automatic or may require workers to place the seed in cups or tubes. (About 90% of the potato crop is planted mechanically)

or

(b) by hand; ridges are opened by a ridging plough, the tubers planted by hand, and the ridges split to cover the tubers.

Spacing of tubers:

(a) Distance between ridges: earlies, 600–650 mm (24–26 in.), main crop 700–900 mm (28–36 in.).

(b) Distance between the tubers (setts) depends on the average size of the tubers and the rate per acre to be planted. Setts averaging 56 grms (2 oz)—about size of hen's egg, planted in 700 mm (28 in.) rows at 2·5 tonne/ha (20 cwt/acre) would be spaced about 300 mm (12 in.) apart.

*Manuring*. Potato crops will benefit from F.Y.M. If it is available, the usual dressing is about 40 t/ha (16 tons/acre). This is either ploughed-in during the autumn or put in the ridges in the spring.

The fertilizers may be broadcast over the open ridges before planting or "placed" in bands by the mechanical planter. Average amounts required may be summarized as follows:

| | N | | $P_2O_5$ | | $K_2O$ | |
|---|---|---|---|---|---|---|
| | kg/ha | units/ acre | kg/ha | units/ acre | kg/ha | units/ acre |
| With 40 t/ha F.Y.M. | 100 | 80 | 100 | 80 | 150 | 120 |
| Without F.Y.M. | 150 | 120 | 150 | 120 | 200 | 160 |

Nitrogen should be reduced to 50 units/acre after good grassland. Potash could be increased to 200 units on low potash soils.

Weeds, by tradition, are controlled by cultivations and ridging after planting but the frequent passage of rubber-tyred tractors tends to produce clods in the ridges and this hinders mechanical harvesting. The cultivations also damage the potato roots and stolons and allow moisture to escape from the soil.

Chemical weed control (see p. 258) with the minimum or no cultivations after planting is now becoming common practice.

Some farmers are now growing potatoes "on the flat" (in beds about 1·5 m wide) instead of ridges; yields are increased but harvesting is difficult on the heavier soils and there is some "greening".

The new tubers in the ridges must be kept covered with soil to protect them from damage by (a) "greening"—due to exposure to light, and (b) blight—due to spores falling onto the tubers from diseased leaves.

*Blight*. This is one of the worst fungous diseases attacking the potato crop. It can seriously reduce yield by killing off the tops (foliage) early. It can also cause rotting of the tubers before or during storage. Some varieties are more resistant to blight than others.

Spraying or dusting with special fungicides can partly control the spread of the disease on the leaves. Chemical or mechanical destruction of the "tops" before the disease kills them completely can reduce the risk of spread of the disease to the tubers. The disease can spread very quickly on the foliage in damp, warm weather.

*Harvesting.* Removal of the green haulms of earlies with a flail type machine immediately before lifting greatly facilitates picking. Maincrops should not be lifted before the skins have hardened on the tubers—this is usually about three weeks after the haulms have died or have been desiccated with *diquat, dinoseb* or *sulphuric acid.*

Mechanical harvesters only work well on soils which have very few stones and clods but where stones and clods have to be picked off by hand the harvesters save a lot of backache compared with picking off the ground. The slow rate of working and mechanical damage to the tubers are problems which are being overcome. Fully automatic harvesters using electronic separating devices have been developed for use on stony and cloddy soils.

Hand-picking is still the main method used. If a *spinner* is used for exposing the tubers then only one row can be picked up at a time. It is more efficient to lift a number of rows ahead of the pickers (one row for each picker). This can be done by several types of *lifters,* e.g. *elevator digger, swinging-sieve type* or *potato plough.*

The pickers put the potatoes into baskets and these are then emptied into trailers alongside or into *stillages* (boxes or containers which can be mechanically handled).

*Storage.* The tubers may be stored in a clamp (pit) in the field and covered with a good layer of straw and 150–300 mm (6–12 in.) of soil to prevent frost damage. Removing the potatoes from clamps in winter is an unpleasant job in bad weather and storage in buildings is the main method used nowadays. In-door stores must be frost-proof and it is common practice to have ventilating ducts under the heaps to allow air to be blown through. In this way sprout-suppressant chemicals, e.g. CIPC, may be introduced or chilled (not frosty) air may be blown through to check sprouting.

The heap should be covered with a deep layer of straw to protect the tubers from frost, light which causes "greening", and to prevent condensation of moisture on the tubers.

The tubers may also be stored in stillages (boxes) in stores or on concrete areas and covered with straw bales and polythene sheets.

*Grading.* The stored tubers are usually riddled (graded or sorted) during the winter or early spring. The best potatoes (ware) are separated from the chats (small tubers), diseased, damaged, over-sized and misshapen tubers. In future an increasing amount of grading and sorting will be done at central grading stations for groups of co-operating farmers. Careful handling at all stages of harvesting and storage is essential to prevent damage to the tubers.

### Sugar-beet

The sugar which is extracted from the crop supplies this country with about one-third of its total sugar requirements.

It is grown on contract for the British Sugar Corporation which has seventeen factories in the British Isles. A contract price per ton of washed beet containing a standard percentage of sugar is determined annually from an agreed acreage by arrangement with the Government and the E.E.C. The price for any beet grown in excess of this acreage is dependent on world prices. A bonus or deduction is made if the sugar content is above or below the standard. The average sugar content is about 17%.

Apart from its sugar, sugar-beet has two useful by-products:

(1) Beet tops—a very succulent food, but which must be fed wilted.

(2) Beet pulp—the residue of the roots after the sugar has been extracted; an excellent feed for stock.

*Yield:* Good average yield of washed roots. 45 tonne/hectare (18 tons/acre) giving about 7·5 tonne/hectare (3 tons/acre) of sugar. Also, 40 tonne/ha (16 tons/acre) of tops. The yield of tops varies with the variety and growing conditions. Stock farmers prefer the large-topped varieties.

*Seed rate* depends on seed spacing, row width and type of seed:
pelleted seed—8–30 kg/ha (7–25 lb/acre).
unpelleted seed—1–12 kg/ha (1–10 lb/acre).

*Time of sowing:* mid–March–mid–April.

*Time of harvesting:* end of September to December.

*Varieties*

The N.I.A.B. recommended list, and the factory field officer will help in deciding upon the variety to be grown. There are many different varieties and they can be grouped according to the yield of roots, the sugar percentage, and their resistance to bolting, i.e. running to seed in the year of sowing. This is influenced by a cold spell in the three- to four-leaf stage of the plant. Bolting is highly undesirable, as the roots become woody with a low sugar content. Varieties with a high resistance to bolting should be used for early sowing and in colder districts.

*Climate and soils.* Sugar-beet is a sun-loving crop which will not grow well when there is too much rain and cloud.

It can be grown on the majority of soils, except heavy clays, which are usually too wet and sticky, and stony soils, which make cultivation and harvesting difficult.

*Place in rotation.* As long as the land is reasonably clean of weeds, the place in rotation is not so important these days. But by law, beet must not be grown too frequently on the same land because of the build-up of eelworm.

*Seed-bed.* The importance of a good seed-bed for sugar-beet cannot be over-emphasized. The success or failure of the crop can, to a great extent, depend on the seed-bed. It must be deep yet firm, fine and level (see page 79).

*Manuring*

(1) *F.Y.M.:* 26 tonne of well rotted manure per hectare (10–12 tons/acre); applied in the autumn.

(2) *Lime:* A soil pH of between 6·5–7·0 is necessary.

(3) *Salt:* ½ tonne/ha (4 cwt/acre) broadcast a few weeks before sowing. This should give nearly ½ tonne extra sugar per hectare.

(4) *Magnesium:* Magnesium deficiency has become more evident in recent years, particularly on light, sandy soils. 400 kg/ha (3 cwt/ acre) Keiserite (magnesium sulphate) should be applied if necessary.

Other plant foods required can be summarized as follows:

|  | N | | $P_2O_5$ | | $K_2O$ | |
|---|---|---|---|---|---|---|
|  | kg/ha | units/acre | kg/ha | units/acre | kg/ha | units/acre |
| With F.Y.M. and salt | 100 | 80 | 50 | 40 | 88 | 70 |
| Without F.Y.M. but including salt | 125 | 100 | 63 | 50 | 125 | 100 |

Kainit can be used at 500–600 kg/ha (4–5 cwt/acre) instead of potash, salt and magnesium (except in severe cases of magnesium deficiency where Keiserite is still necessary). It should be applied some weeks before sowing the seed.

Trial work shows that additional nitrogen (about 50 kg/ha (40 units/acre)) may be worthwhile, particularly after a wet winter when nitrogen reserves may be low.

The fertilizer can be broadcast and worked into the soil during seed-bed preparations.

*The seed and sowing.* The so-called beet seed is really a cluster of seeds fused together, and it usually produces more than one plant when it germinates. This "natural seed" is no longer used.

In order to make it easier to single the crop three different types of seed are now used:

(1) *Genetical monogerm seed.* Most of the seed contains a single embryo, from which only one plant will grow. Under laboratory conditions, these varieties produce a minimum of 90% single plants.

(2) *Processed multigerm diploid seed* is used which has been seperated out from the cluster. It is known as rubbed and graded gravity separated seed—size 3–4 mm (8–10/64 in.). The use of this seed increases the proportion of single plants by as much as 15% compared with the "natural seed".

(3) *Processed multigerm polyploid seed* is seed in which the chromosome number in the cell nuclei has been increased. It is rubbed and graded to a size of 3·5–4·75 mm (9–12/64 in.). In addition to having a higher natural monogermity (laboratory monogermity—70%)

than the diploids, polploid varieties tend to have a higher sugar percentage, as well as being comparable in yield to diploids.

*Pelleted seed.* Over 90% of the crop sown is with pelleted seed, i.e. it is coated with clay to produce pellets of uniform size and density—3·50–4·75 mm (9–12/64 in.). This is important for mono-germ seed which is rather lens shape, and as such it cannot be handled so well in the precision drill. Pelleted processed multigerm seed is also an improvement.

The crop should be sown in 450–550 mm (18–22 in.) rows; great care must be taken to see that the drills or rows of plants are as straight and evenly spaced as possible because of subsequent inter-row work.

Shallower sowing will aid quicker germination: 18–25 mm ($\frac{3}{4}$–1 in.) is ideal with a well prepared seed-bed. A press wheel fitted immediately behind the seed coulter effectively compresses the soil over the seed, and in dry weather this will help germination.

*Treatment during the growing period.* The crop should emerge in weed-free conditions using chemical weed control (see page 258.). But as soon as the seedlings can be seen as continuous lines across the field, steerage hoeing should also be carried out to assist in weed control, and to ease the work of singling.

(1) *Singling* (thinning). Ideally this should be done at the four-to-six-leaf stage. Delaying it much after this can mean a reduction in field yield.

Singling by hand is usually done at piecework rates. The final average distance apart of the plants in the row must depend upon the row widths, i.e. rows of 500 mm (20 in.) apart—plants thinned to 225 mm (9 in.) apart, or rows of 550 mm (22 in.) apart—plants thinned to 200 mm (8 in.) apart. This will give a plant population approaching the ideal 73,000–86,000/ha (30,000–35,000/acre).

Further inter-row work can be carried out to check the weeds, and these hoeings may be continued until the beet leaves meet across the rows, but if the soil is dry, too much working must be avoided.

Mechanical singling of the crop has never been a very successful practice, but it is suggested that it could now have better possibilities starting with a thinner row.

*Drilling to a stand.* At present about 40% of the sugar beet crop is "drilled to a stand", i.e. the individual seeds are placed separately in the position required for the plant. It is expected that in a few years almost all the crop will be grown in this way.

The introduction of monogerm seed, the re-introduction of pelleting for both monogerm and processed multigerm seed, precision drilling together with the use of efficient herbicides has certainly enhanced the chances of success.

The main aim of "drilling to a stand" is to have a reasonably spaced yet adequate plant population. When this is less than 60,000 plants/ha (about 25,000/acre) there is usually a serious reduction in final yield.

Depending on soil conditions and varietal percentage field emergence, the seed spacing should be at 120–175 mm (5–7 in.).

A weed-free seed bed is essential because there will be no opportunity for removing weeds as with normal singling operations, and so the technique is entirely dependent on adequate weed control by chemical means.

Apart from the saving in labour costs, another important advantage of the technique is that compared with conventional growing the need with larger acreages to space out the actual drilling no longer arises. Thus the seed can be sown under the best possible conditions.

Evidence shows that provided it is successfully carried out, and this means one mature plant for every two seeds sown, there is no difference in final yield comparing "drilling to a stand" with conventional growing.

*Virus yellows.* It may be necessary to spray the crop to kill the aphids which spread virus yellows (Table 22), or to apply the insecticide as granules spread on the soil.

*Harvesting.* In theory, early November is the right time to harvest the beet crop. Although it is still slightly increasing in weight the sugar percentage is beginning to fall off.

But, of course, if all beet were delivered at this time there would be tremendous congestion at the factory. Therefore a permit delivery system is used, whereby each grower is given dated loading permits which operate from the end of September until about the end of January. It means that growers must be prepared to have their beet delivered to the factory at intervals throughout the period upon receiving prior notice from the factory.

The crop is now all mechanically harvested. Topping must be done accurately (see Fig. 37). Overtopping can result in a serious loss of yield, and undertopping means paying extra carriage for unwanted material. The modern complete harvester either tops, lifts and delivers the beet into a vehicle running alongside, or after topping and lifting collects the beet in a self-unloading tank on the harvester. Most sugar beet harvesters can be fitted with "top-savers" which leave the tops in clean condition for subsequent feeding. The tank-harvester (normally 1 or 2 row) has many

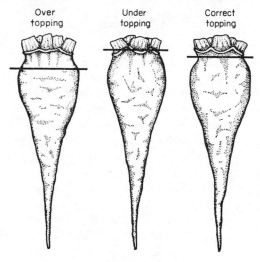

Fig. 37.

advantages, not least of which is that harvesting can be operated on a one-man system. Multi-stage machines have now been re-introduced. They deal with either 3, 5 or 6 rows. With the 6-row, for example, the system consists of a 6-windrowing topper in the first stage, followed by a 6-row lifter in the second stage, with harvesting completed in the third stage by the roots being picked up from the

6-row windrows. It is capable of harvesting at a rate of nearly ½ ha (about 1 acre) per hour.

To minimize dirt tares direct delivery from field to factory should be avoided, especially when the beet are harvested in wet conditions. If the beet can be clamped at least a week before delivery, and then re-loaded using an elevator with a cleaning mechanism, dirt tares will be considerably reduced. Beet stored on the farm should be covered to prevent damage by frost.

### Mangolds

The mangold is grown for feeding to cattle and sheep in the more southerly parts of the country, where it is a more certain cropper than swedes and turnips, although its popularity has declined markedly in recent years. In the wetter and cooler regions swedes and turnips crops are preferable. It contains less than 14% dry matter, and is quite susceptible to frost injury. Because of this, the crop is harvested before it is mature, but it should not be fed until after Christmas, when it has ripened off in the clamp. The tops are of no value. The growing of mangolds is similar to sugar-beet as regards soil and climate, seed-bed preparations, and general fertilizer treatment.

*Yield per hectare:* 50–100 tonne (20–40 tons/acre).

*Seed rate per hectare:* 7–9 kg (6–8 lb/acre) with processed seed.

*Sowing:* April to early May, in rows (22–24 in.) apart. Unnecessarily wide rows reduce the yield; the ultimate aim should be 60,000 plants to the hectare (25,000/acre).

*Varieties:* Globes, Tankards (oblong-shaped), Longs, Intermediates (in shape between the Globe and the Long).

Treatment during the growing period can follow the same pattern as for sugar-beet, although singling is usually started when the plants are in the two- to three-leaf stage.

*Harvesting.* November is the normal time to harvest the crop They are simply pulled out, and because they "bleed" very easily, the tops (not the crowns) are either cut or twisted off. The roots are left untrimmed.

After a period of "sweating out" in the field in small heaps covered with leaves, the mangolds must be carefully clamped. They should be built up as large as they can be conveniently heaped, and then covered with a good layer of straw. This will be sufficient in sheltered areas away from frost, but otherwise soil on top of the straw will have to be used in addition.

### Fodder Beet

This plant has been bred from selections from sugar-beet and mangolds. It aroused great interest in this country during and just after the Second World War because of its value in pig feeding. It has a higher dry matter content than the mangold and it is quite useful in the fattening of pigs, although there is very little grown now. Fodder beet can be fed immediately after lifting, and the tops after wilting are also valuable. Its growing is very similar to that of mangolds.

### Turnips and Swedes

They are the most widely grown root crops in the northern and western regions of the country. Although their popularity has declined markedly in the last twenty years, new methods of growing and harvesting these crops could result in a reversal of this trend. In appearance, the difference between the two crops is that turnips have hairy, grass-green leaves which arise direct from the bulb itself, and swedes have smooth ashy-green leaves which grow out from an extended stem or "neck". Nutritionally, swedes are more valuable than turnips as they have a higher dry matter content. The turnip has a shorter growing period and some varieties (notably those from the Continent) are being increasingly used for catch-cropping (page 122).

Both are valuable for cattle and sheep and, depending on the variety grown, they can be used as table vegetables. A limited market is developing for contract growing for freezing.

*Main crops–yield per·hectare–*turnips, 50 tonne (20 tons/acre); swedes, 50–85 tonne (20–35 tons/acre).

*Seed rate per hectare:* 0·5–4·5 kg ($\frac{1}{2}$–4 lb/acre) (lower amount with the precision drill which is now more often the case) in rows 500–550 mm (20–22 in.) apart. Turnips can also be broadcast at 4·5–7 kg (4–6 lb/acre).

Dual–purpose seed dressings, containing gamma–BHC as a protection against flea–beetle, and thiram for protection against soil–borne fungus, should be used.

*Time of sowing:* mid–April to end of June.

*Climate and soil.* The crops like a cool, moist climate without too much sunshine. Most soils (except heavy clays) are suitable.

*Seed–bed.* A fine, firm and moist seed–bed is necessary to get the plant quickly established. In very wet districts the crops can, with advantage, be sown on the ridge (see p. 79).

The plant foods required can be summarized as follows:—

| | N | | $P_2O_5$ | | $K_2O$ | |
|---|---|---|---|---|---|---|
| | kg/ha | units/ acre | kg/ha | units/ acre | kg/ha | units/ acre |
| With F.Y.M. | 50 | 40 | 50–75 | 40–60 | 50 | 40 |
| Without F.Y.M. | 50–100 | 40–80 | 100–112 | 80–90 | 100 | 80 |

F.Y.M.—25–40 tonne/ha (10–15 tons/acre) is applied in the autumn. This is especially important for improving the water–holding capacity of the lighter soils.

The lower amount of nitrogen is used in wetter areas and more phosphate is needed on heavier soils.

Lime is most essential. Soil pH should be above 6·0. Finger and toe disease can be prevalent under acid conditions. However, over–liming is equally serious as it can cause RAAN or Heart rot (Table 21).

*Varieties*

| Varieties | Feed Value | Remarks |
|---|---|---|
| *Turnips*<br>White-fleshed | Low | Heavy croppers; poor keepers; can be grown as a catch crop, as well as a main crop. |
| Yellow-fleshed | High | Slowest to mature; keeping quality good; require fertile conditions for best results. |
| *Swedes*<br>(grouped according to skin colour) | | |
| Light-purple | Generally low | Normally quickest to mature and heaviest yielder. |
| Dark-purple | Medium to high | Not heavy yielding. Highly resistant to frost damage. Suited more to conditions in Scotland. |
| Green | High | Later to mature and fairly hardy, many varieties are resistant to club-root disease. |
| Bronze | Very mixed varieties as regards yield, time of maturity and hardiness. | |

For more details of varieties see the N.I.A.B. recommended list

The stale seedbed technique using a contact herbicide to kill the weeds at the time of drilling is now considered an effective method of weed control (page 88), but it is still more normal to carry out inter-row cultivations which will follow the same lines as with most root crops. These cultivations, with the use of chemicals, will keep the crop clean (page 259). There is an increasing tendency not to thin precision-drilled crops. The low seed rate with precision-drilling should mean a spacing of between 125–175 mm (5–7 in.), otherwise it will be advisable to rough single to 250 mm (10 in.) apart. This is normally done at the two-to-four-leaf stage.

*Harvesting turnips.* The main crop is ready for lifting and feeding in October when the outer leaves begin to decay. They can be stored in one main clamp (the leaves may be left on) in a similar way to mangolds.

In mild districts yellow turnips can be left growing in the field and removed as required, or they may be stored in small, roughly covered heaps in the field.

Both white and yellow turnips, but particularly white turnips, are often grazed off in the field.

*Harvesting swedes.* In most districts swedes are lifted about November, before they are fully matured. It is therefore advisable to allow roots to ripen off in a clamp to minimize scouring when later feeding to stock. In fact, in mild districts they may be left growing to mature in the field. Special machines are now available for the complete harvesting of the crop. A 74 tonne/ha (30 ton/acre) crop can be topped, lifted and elevated into a trailer at a rate of about one-tenth of a hectare (nearly one-third of an acre) per hour.

Swedes, like turnips, are very often grazed off in the field.

### Kale

Kale is grown for feeding to livestock, usually in the autumn and winter months. It can be fed either on the field, or, it can be cut (normally with a forage harvester) and carted off for feeding green or making into silage, and in these cases a heavier yielding crop is needed.

*Yield:* 37–74 tonnes/ha (15–30 t/acre).

*Time of sowing:* end of March–mid-July. Early sowing gives heavier crops but these are more susceptible to frost damage.

*Seed rate:* 1–4 kg/ha (1–3 lb/acre) *drilled* in 350–600 mm (14–24 in.) rows; 4·5–7 kg (4–6 lb) *broadcast*. The seed should be dressed with gamma-BHC as a protection against flea-beetle.

*Types of kale*

| | |
|---|---|
| Marrow stem | 1 metre tall (3–4 ft). Thick stems and large leaves. Produces heavy crops of good digestibility (see page 209) but not winter hardy. Use before the new year. |
| Thousand-head | About 1 metre tall. Much branched plant with numerous small leaves. Hardier, but less palatable and digestible than marrow stem. |
| Dwarf-thousand-head | Useful for feeding in late winter. Shows a considerable growth of new shoots late in the winter. Shorter stemmed but more palatable and digestible than thousand-head. |
| Other types | Hybrid varieties such as Maris Kestrel and Proteor have recently been produced. Maris Kestrel is less than 1 metre high, and although it is a marrow stem kale it is as winter hardy as thousand-head. Being shorter-stemmed it is ideally suited for grazing and is very digestible. |

With any type of kale it is important to choose a reliable variety within the type.

The N.I.A.B. recommended list will give advice on varieties.

*Climate and soil.* Kale is a very adaptable crop, although under very dry conditions it may be a little difficult to get it well established. For folding, it is preferable to grow it under drier, lighter soil conditions, or on well drained soils.

*Manuring.* F.Y.M.—up to 50 tonne/hectare (20 tons/acre)—is applied in the autumn. It is especially important when a heavy yielding crop is the aim.

Other plant foods required can be summarized as follows:

| | N | | $P_2O_5$ | | $K_2O$ | |
|---|---|---|---|---|---|---|
| | kg/ha | units/acre | kg/ha | units/acre | kg/ha | units/acre |
| With F.Y.M. | 125 | 100 | 63 | 50 | 63 | 50 |
| Without F.Y.M. | 150 | 120 | 125 | 100 | 125 | 100 |

The fertilizer is usually applied during final seed-bed preparations. Although placement of fertilizer and seed can be carried out there is no great improvement in final yield.

*Seed-bed.* A fine, firm, and clean seed-bed is required. But the crop can be "direct-drilled" (slit-seeded) and this has the important advantages of conserving moisture at sowing time and leaving a much firmer surface for grazing and good annual weed control.

*Treatment during the growing period.* With drilled crops, steerage hoeing may have to be carried out a number of times from an early stage, but the herbicide desmetryne has eased the problem of keeping the crop weed-free (see p. 259).

If necessary, the crop should be dusted against flea-beetles.

The drilled crop is seldom singled. With a precision-drilled crop, the aim should be to produce a plant every 75–150 mm (3–6 in.) in the row. With an unthinned crop a higher proportion of leaf to stem is obtained which produces more succulent plants. Sometimes the crop is harrowed across to make it thinner.

*Utilizing the crop.* With cattle, grazing in the field using the electric fence avoids the laborious job of cutting and carting the crop. But light or well drained soils are essential, otherwise both stock and soil suffer; cutting before fencing reduces waste.

To avoid wet and sticky conditions which normally get worse towards the end of the year, the tendency these days is to start feeding kale to dairy cows much earlier in the autumn, although in a mild season it will continue to grow on well into early winter.

If strip-grazing is not possible, the forage-harvester may be used to chop the crop coarsely and blow it into a trailer, or it can be cut with an old mower.

## Cabbages

Cabbages have a wide range of uses. They are a useful food for all classes of stock and, when suitable varieties are grown, high value crops can be produced for human consumption. These can be fed to stock when the market price is too low.

Cabbages prefer moist, heavy soils, and seasons with plenty of rainfall, but apart from this the same growing conditions suit cabbage as kale. They respond to plenty of fertilizer, but too much nitrogen (not more than 112 kg/ha (90 units/acre), can cause the hearts to split. 200 kg/ha (180 units/acre) $P_2O_5$ and 225 kg/ha (180 units/acre) $K_2O$ should also be applied.

*Varieties.* There are a large number of varieties which can be roughly grouped as follows:

|  | Sown | Planted out | Ready for consumption |  |
|---|---|---|---|---|
| Early | March May August | April, May June, July Following April September | August–September October onwards July March–June | Can be used for stock and human consumption. |
| Late *or* Maincrop | August August | Following April October | September July onwards | Chiefly used for stock feeding. |

A reliable variety should be chosen within these groups, and the N.I.A.B. recommended list will give details of varieties of flat poll cabbage. The seed is normally sown in specially prepared seed-beds. About 1 kg of seed gives sufficient plants for planting one hectare (1 lb/acre). 75 kg/ha of superphosphate (60 units/acre) should be broadcast before sowing. For planting out, a transplanter can be used. They are best planted on the square, i.e. approximately 600 mm (2 ft) between the plants and 600 mm (2 ft) between the rows. This will help in later cultivations. There is now an increasing tendency to space-drill the crop with the seed placed either three at a time— 25 mm (1 in.) apart, or single-spaced 100 mm (4 in.) in the row. The plants are eventually thinned down to the required distances apart.

### Brussels Sprouts

Brussels sprouts can be grown on a commercial scale in most parts of the country, and they do not require exacting soil conditions.

The growing and marketing of the crop should now be considered in two different ways:

(1) for the fresh market or successive picking,

(2) for quick freezing or single harvesting.

1. THE FRESH MARKET

*Yield* 15–20 tonnes/ha (6–8 tons/acre).

The management is similar to that for cabbage growing. Plants can be raised from seed in a seedbed using approximately ½ kg of seed for every hectare to be planted.

The seed is sown (1) in August (earlier enough to withstand the winter) to be planted out in March and April, ready for picking late August and September

or (2) from mid-January to mid-March in batches to be planted out from April to June ready for picking October to March according to variety and season.

The plants are normally planted out "on the square" from 750 to 900 mm (30 to 36 in.) apart.

Like cabbages, they may be space-drilled in rows 900 mm (36 in.) apart with the seed dropped in groups of three every 600 mm (24 in.) apart for medium sized sprouts, or every 900 mm (36 in.) apart where high yielding large sprouts are required. Alternatively a seed may be dropped every 100 mm (4 in.) apart. In both cases, surplus plants are removed when large enough.

Graded seed is now available covering a range 1·75–2·5 mm (5–6/64 in.) in diameter.

*Varieties.* Medium to large sprouts—*Early* up to mid-October, e.g. Early Half Tall from Denmark and Early F1 hybrids.

*Mid-Season.* Mid-October to end December, e.g. Roodnerf selections from Holland and mid-season F1 hybrids.

*Late.* After December, e.g. Roodnerf late selections.

Vegetable Growers Leaflet No. 3 will give further details.

*Manuring.* The plant foods required can be summarized as follows:

|  | N | | $P_2O_5$ | | $K_2O$ | |
|---|---|---|---|---|---|---|
|  | kg/ha | units/ acre | kg/ha | units/ acre | kg/ha | units/ acre |
| With F.Y.M. | 150 | 120 | 75 | 60 | 105 | 85 |
| Without F.Y.M. | 190 | 150 | 125 | 100 | 225 | 180 |

*Nirtogen top-dressing* will be required for the crop at anything from 0 to 190 kg/ha (0 to 150 units) depending upon the appearance of the crop. The F1 hybrids generally require a heavier top-dressing.

*Treatment during the growing period.* This will generally follow the same procedure as for the cabbage crop. Instead of inter-row hoeings, and depending on the weeds present, desmetryne and sodium monochloracetate may be used at the seedling weed stage. The use of a pre-emergence weedkiller will also reduce subsequent inter-row work.

Control measures may be necessary against the cabbage root fly, aphis and caterpillar.

*Stopping or cocking the plants.* By removing the growing point (or terminal bud) from the plant, sprout growth is stimulated so that harvesting may be carried out at an earlier date. Stopping takes place from early August to about the third week in October. Plants should be stopped about five weeks before the expected picking time, but there is no point in stopping after October.

*Harvesting.* Picking usually starts in early September and extends until March according to the variety and season. For maximum yield, the plants are picked over four to eight times during the season.

### 2. FOR FREEZING

Varieties producing medium-size sprouts are necessary for these crops grown on contract for the frozen food market.

*Varieties.* F1 hybrids such as Lancelot, Topscore, and non-hybrids such as Roodnerf selections.

The growing of the crop is similar to that for the fresh market, although present experience indicates February nursery sowings (in cold frames) for harvesting up to the middle of October, and outdoor sowings in March for picking from mid-October till the end of the year.

Space-drilling is normally carried out in April and May.

For mid-season optimum yields, the plants should be grown on a 525 mm (21 in.) square, but up to a 675 mm (27 in.) square for the earlier August harvesting.

*Harvesting.* At present harvesting of the single-pick crop consists of deleafing the stems by hand immediately before the stems are cut either by hand or machine for feeding into the sprout-stripping machine. The sprouts are then graded by riddling.

### Carrots

The common yellow carrots may be grown on contract for canning or quick-freezing but most of the crop is sold as a vegetable—either as fully grown clean roots or as bunches of young carrots. Unsaleable and surplus roots can be fed to stock (usually cattle); the white cattle carrots are not grown in this country now.

*Yield of roots:* average, 30 t/ha (12 tons/acre); good, 60 t/ha (24 tons/acre).

*Soils and climate.* The climate in most parts of this country is suitable for carrots but the main growing areas are limited by soil conditions. Carrots can only be grown successfully on a farm scale on deep sandy loams and black fen soils, mainly because it is easy to lift and clean the roots. Stony and shallow soils produce badly shaped roots which may be unsaleable.

*Seed-bed:* should be fine, firm, clean and level (as for sugar-beet). If there is a pan in the soil it must be broken by sub soiling.

*Varieties.* There are many good varieties which are grouped by the shape of root as *long, stump-rooted* and *intermediate.* The latter are the most common type.

*Sowing.* The seed, which usually has the bristles machined off it, may be sown shallow 10–30 mm ($\frac{1}{2}$–1 in. deep) in:

    (a) wide rows 450–500 mm (18–20 in.)—weeds controlled by inter-row cultivations.

    (b) narrow rows 150–200 mm (6–8 in.) or in beds 1–1·5 metres ($3$–$4\frac{1}{2}$ ft) wide—weeds controlled by chemicals.

The yield from (b) is very much greater due to the high plant population per acre.

*Seed rate.* Up to 5 kg/ha (4 lb/acre) is sown where the crop is singled. This is not a common practice now when it is more usual to sow about 1–2 kg/ha ($1$–$1\frac{1}{2}$ lb/acre) with a precision drill and leave all plants to mature.

*Time of sowing:* main crops—April, but varies from late February to March.

*Manuring.* F.Y.M. can be beneficial on sandy soils but it must be well rotted and ploughed in deeply in the autumn. The fertilizers used on average fertility soils without F.Y.M. should contain about 55 kg/ha (45 units/acre) N, 100 kg/ha (80 units/acre) $P_2O_5$ and 125 kg/ha (100 units/acre) $K_2O$. 375 kg/ha (3 cwt/acre) of salt may be applied several weeks before sowing and the potash reduced to 60 kg/ha (50 units/acre).

*Chemical weed control.* This has greatly simplified carrot growing on many farms. Contact chemicals can be used to kill seedling weeds before the crop emerges (as in sugar-beet, see p. 259), or, most tractor vaporizing oils and some specially selected mineral oils can be used, when the carrots are in the seedling stage, to kill a wide range of weeds. Pre-emergent treatment with linuron or prometryne gives very good weed control; both these herbicides can also be used as post-emergence sprays. (See M.A.F.F. STL leaflet No. 29.)

*Harvesting.* This usually starts in October and may continue well into the winter in areas where severe frost is not likely to cause damage. The crop is either lifted by hand or by various types of modified root harvesters.

*Storage.* Usually in small clamps with the soil in direct contact with the roots to help keep them fresh looking. Some are now stored indoors. For many markets it is now necessary to wash the carrots (usually by machines) before sale. They are often sold in net bags.

## Bulb Onions

Both bulb and salad onions are grown in this country, but the latter are mainly grown by market gardeners because of the large amount of casual labour required for harvesting (see M.A.F.F. Advisory leaflet No. 358, Salad Onions).

Bulb onions have increased in importance very rapidly recently because of the very high prices paid in some years, and because of precision drilling, improved chemical weed, pest and disease control, and better methods of harvesting and storage.

About half of our total requirements—350,000 tons—of bulb onions are home-grown and there is plenty of scope for increased production provided it is good quality.

The ripened onion consists of edible, swollen, leaf bases surrounded by scale leaves with withered tips. Bulb onions can now be supplied to our markets throughout the year because of modern developments in storage, and the production of autumn-sown crops, which in mild areas, can be harvested from June onwards until the spring-sown crops are ready.

*Yields.* These are variable, usually 30–50 tonne/ha (12–20 tons/acre).

*Soils and climate.* Bulb onions can be grown in many parts of this country, but do best in the eastern and south-eastern counties.

They can be grown on a wide range of mineral and peat soils provided they are well drained, have a good available-water capacity, have a pH of 6·5 or over, and are friable enough to produce good seedbeds: shallow soils, thin chalk, dry sands, and sticky clays are not suitable. If growth is stopped by drought and a secondary growth follows after rain, the outer layers of the bulb may split open.

*Rotation.* Onions and crops such as field and broad beans, oats, and parsnips, which carry the same pests, should not normally be grown more often than one year in five on the same field because of the risk of eelworm, onion fly and white rot disease.

*Seedbed.* A fine, firm, moist, clean, level and pan-free tilth is required.

*Varieties.* A wide range of varieties are available—mostly of the Rijnsburger type—for spring sowing; and Japanese, non-bolting types for autumn sowing.

*Time of sowing.* As soon as possible after mid–February provided the seedbed is in good condition; the seedlings can stand slight frosts. The formation of new green leaves and the start of bulb formation is associated with long days of 14–16 hours, i.e. late May and June, so it is important to get the crop established early. Over-wintering crops are usually sown in late August or early September.

*Sowing.* Onions should be sown with a precision drill in shallow 12–20 mm ($\frac{1}{2}$–$\frac{3}{4}$ in.) rows which may be spaced in various ways, e.g. double rows at 500 mm (20 in.) centres.

*Seed rate.* Graded seed 4–6 kg/ha (3-5 lb/acre), or pelleted seed up to 28 kg/ha. The aim should be about 7 plants per square foot.

*Fertilizers.* For good to average conditions, 100 kg/ha (80 units/ acre) of N and $P_2O_5$ and 200 kg/ha (160 units/acre), of $K_2O$.

*Weed control.* Good weed control over a long period is essential for good yields. This usually means using a pre-emergence herbicide such as *propachlor* ("Ramrod") or pyrazone/chlorbufam ("Alicep"), to be followed by post-emergent treatment with Alicep, Ramrod, *ioxynil* ("Totril"), or *methazole* ("Paxilon"), to control the common annual weeds. Couch and other perennial weeds should be destroyed in previous years. (See M.A.F.F. leaflet STL No. 73.)

*Harvesting.* Bulb onions are ready for harvesting when most of the tops have fallen over—usually in early September. If left later, yields might be slightly better, but the outer skins are likely to crack and so cause serious disease losses in store. Maleic hydracide, sprayed on the ripening crop, can prevent much sprouting in storage. The crop is usually harvested in two stages—first, the bulbs are lifted out of the ground by a horizontal tine or share and several rows put into one windrow. After drying for a few days they are elevated into a trailer.

*Storage.* The bulbs can be stored in bulk stores up to 3 metres (10 ft) deep with ventilation ducts underneath, or in boxes or bins of various sizes. They should be dried as soon as possible by blowing with slightly heated air. Temperature and humidity during drying and storage are very important; onions remain dormant (i.e. no sprouting) at low (32°F) and high (80°F) temperatures; humidity can affect skin colour. (See M.A.F.F. leaflet STL No. 136, Buildings for Onion Drying and Storage.)

Onions are usually graded into various sizes before sale, for example, over $2\frac{1}{4}$ in., $1\frac{3}{4}$–$2\frac{1}{4}$ in., $1\frac{1}{4}$–$1\frac{3}{4}$ in., and picklers.

*Diseases and pests. Neck rot (bulb rot)*—a very serious problem—especially in some seasons. Control benomyl ('Benlate') seed dressing and/or foliage sprays, and quick drying in store. *White rot*—soil-borne fungus causing rotting of roots and base of bulb. Control by wide rotation and *calomel* seed dressing. *Onion fly*—maggots eat into developing bulb—especially in June and July. Control with dieldrin seed dressing. (See M.A.F.F. Advisory leaflet No. 163.)

## Vegetable Production on Farms

Farm-scale vegetable production is becoming increasingly important in many areas since the introduction of precision drills, safe and efficient herbicides and pesticides, mechanical harvesting and improved storage methods. This type of crop production is much more demanding of mental energy but can be very satisfying if well done. Profits can be higher than for ordinary farm crops, but costs and risks of failures are also high. It is very important to know what the market wants and to produce only what is wanted, when it is wanted, and in the quantities and quality required. If possible contracts should be arranged with buyers such as processors, pre-packers, supermarkets, chain stores and co-operatives. Limiting factors may be soil type, distance from markets, suitable labour and supervision, and if pre-packing on the farm a suitable building and a clean water supply may be necessary.

The main vegetable crops now being grown on a field scale are: broad, green and navy beans; vining and dried peas; Brussels sprouts; cabbages; carrots; cauliflowers; celery; onions; turnips and swedes.

It is outside the scope of this book to deal with these very specialized crops in detail, but some information on the more important ones is included. Further details can be obtained from M.A.F.F. Bulletins and leaflets, from A.D.A.S. and commercial advisory services, and from The National Vegetable Research Station.

### Seed Production

Under E.E.C. regulations, in being or being introduced, all seeds sold to farmers must be officially controlled, certified, tested, sealed and labelled.

Detailed standards for acceptable varieties, purity and trueness to type, freedom from seed-borne pests and diseases, tolerances for contamination with weed seeds and rubbish, and viability, are laid down for each type of crop.

Seed production from crops such as *cereals*, *beans* and *peas* is carried out in much the same way as growing ordinary grain crops but special care must be taken with regard to the previous cropping of the field, the grade of seed sown, avoidance of weed seed con-tamination (especially wild oats in cereals), diseases such as loose smut in cereals and ascochyta in beans, and priority at harvest, drying temperatures, careful cleaning and storage to avoid damaging or contaminating the seed. Very good prices are now paid for seed crops which are produced to the required standards.

*Potatoes.* Seed potato production has, traditionally, been mainly carried on in Scotland, Northern Ireland, and the hill areas of England and Wales, and this is how it will continue under E.E.C. regulations. In these areas, the lower temperatures and stronger winds keep the greenfly (aphid) populations in check and so the severe virus diseases (leaf-roll and mosaics), which are spread from diseased to healthy plants by aphids, are less likely to occur. All seed crops must be certified during the growing season to ensure that they are true to type and variety, and are as free as possible from virus and other diseases; the fields in which they are grown must also be tested and found to be free of potato cyst eelworm. The top grade of seed is V.T.S.C. (Virus Tested from Stem Cutting); this is first produced by rooting stem cuttings of virus-free plants in sterilized compost; this method ensures freedom from tuber-borne diseases such as gangrene, skin spot and blackleg; great care must be taken when handling these stocks to prevent contamination from diseased stocks. F.S. (Foundation Seed) and Class AA are the next grades and are also suitable for further seed production. Grade CC is the lowest grade and can only be used for ware production. Seed crops should, ideally, be sprouted before planting and a high seed rate used to ensure a good yield of seed-size tubers ($1\frac{1}{4}$–$1\frac{1}{2}$ in.); the haulms should be destroyed chemically or otherwise when most of the tubers are of seed size, and this also reduces the risk of spread of virus diseases. The harvested crop is usually inspected and the bags of seed tubers sealed on the farm before despatch to other growers. Ware potato growers sometimes save their own seed from crops which have been sprayed with a systemic aphicide and so they need not buy in new seed every year. Seed potato crops should not be grown on the same field more often than one year in five.

*Grasses.* Grass seed production can be very profitable in favourable seasons and if done properly; it requires considerable skill and perseverence, and good yields are very dependent on good growing conditions, and dry weather during the critical harvesting period. The Italian ryegrasses can be harvested for one season only, but most of the perennial grasses will produce two or more seed crops. This type of ley is deep-rooting and is very good for building up humus and good soil structure as well as providing hay and some grazing (the latter is improved if some white clover is sown with the grass). It is very important that there are no grass weeds in the field—especially blackgrass, and other cultivated grass species with similar sized seed: also, about 200 metres isolation is necessary to avoid cross-pollination with grasses in other fields. The ryegrasses and fescues are usually undersown in spring cereals or oil-seed rape, in narrow rows or broadcast, whereas, cocksfoot and timothy are usually sown in wide rows (about 500 mm) and not undersown. A good ryegrass crop will usually "lodge" about a fortnight before harvest and this will reduce losses by wind. Harvesting is in July or early August (timothy in late August or September), and the crop may be combined direct or from windrows—timing is critical. The seed must be carefully dried and cleaned. (See also M.A.F.F. Bulletin No. 204.)

*Clovers.* Seed is usually broadcast and undersown in a cereal crop. The red clovers are usually harvested once (in the following year) after taking a silage cut. Late flowering red may be left to produce a second seed crop. The simplest method of harvesting (usually in September) is to destroy most of the leafy growth with a contact chemical (e.g. dinoseb, diquat, pentachlorphenol, or sulphuric acid) and then combine direct.

White clover is often sown with perennial ryegrass or meadow fescue. Successful harvesting is very dependent on good weather. In a bad season it may pay to collect the crop with a forage harvester and dry it carefully on a grass drier before threshing.

*Sugar-beet, mangolds, fodder beet.* These biennial plants produce seed in the year following sowing. Some of the seed is grown in special zoned areas (to avoid cross-fertilization) in the eastern counties. Young plants (stecklings) are grown in narrows rows from seed sown about July. It is desirable that the stecklings should be produced well away from the main sugar-beet areas (e.g. in the seed potato areas) to avoid carrying over virus yellows. The stecklings may be transplanted in the autumn or following spring from the special seed-beds in which they are grown, or left to grow on to seed. Some stecklings are now undersown (in rows) in a cereal crop or sown after a winter barley crop, and allowed to grow on for seed the following year. Most seed crops are now harvested by combine in early September from windrows cut by a special swathing machine.

*Kales, swedes, turnips, rapes, etc.*, are also biennial plants which produce seed in the year following sowing. Swedes and turnips sown in August and September are usually hardy enough to over-winter. Special precautions have to be taken to avoid cross-fertiliz-ation. They are harvested in late summer—usually combined direct or from a windrow.

Detailed information on the production of seed from these and many other crops are given in N.I.A.B. seed production leaflets.

## Suggestions for Classwork

1. If possible, visit a flour mill, a maltings, an oat processing mill; a sugar-beet factory and a seed cleaning plant.
2. Examine good and bad samples of all the cereal grains.
3. Visit growing crops of cereals, potatoes, roots, peas and beans, etc.
4. When visiting farms see and discuss the various methods used for handling and storing cereals and potatoes.
5. Make notes on the fertilizers used for the crops you visit.
6. Learn how to recognize the different cereals in the leafy stage.
7. Examine potato tubers stored in sprouting boxes and note the controlling effect of light on size of sprouts; see the colour differences between sprouts of different varieties.
8. Note that the haulms of different potato varieties vary in many ways—this is the only sure method of recognizing potato varieties.
9. Visit growing crops of peas and discuss how they are grown and harvested and the problems involved (e.g. damage by pigeons).
10. Examine the different types of sugar-beet seed.
11. Visit sugar-beet crops at singling and harvesting times and discuss the problems involved.

CHAPTER 5

# GRASSLAND

GRASS is the most important crop in this country. About two-thirds of all the farmland is grass, although it is only about one-third in the drier, sunny, eastern areas. Moreover, it is well to remember that grass is a crop, not something which just grows in a field!

**Types of Grassland**

In the British Isles grassland can be broadly divided into three groups:

## 1. ROUGH MOUNTAIN AND HILL GRAZINGS

The plants making up this type of grassland are not of great value. They mainly consist of fescues, bents, nardus and molinia grasses, as well as cotton grass, heather and gorse. Only sheep and beef cattle rearing at very low stocking rates are possible. In some areas where the soil is extremely acid, reafforestation is being successfully carried out.

## 2. PERMANENT PASTURES

These are pastures which are never ploughed. This group covers a wide range, and the quality usually depends on the amount of perennial ryegrass present. A first-grade ryegrass permanent pasture contains over 30% of perennial ryegrass, and this is capable of maintaining a heavy stocking rate. The poorest permanent pastures are not much better than moorland.

3. LEYS

These are temporary swards which have been sown to grass for a limited period (1–4 years). In most cases they will produce more than permanent pastures due to the more productive plants which make up the sward. But this sward will not stand up so well to treading as the permanent pasture.

### Plants making up the Ley

These can be grouped as follows:
*Grasses*
*Legumes:* (a) clovers
  (b) lucerne and sainfoin.
*Herbs*

The grasses and clovers can be divided into *varieties* (cultivars) and further divided into *strains*. There are often important growth differences between strains, for example, the hay strains are earlier to start growth in the spring, earlier to flower, have a taller habit of growth, more flowering stems, and are less leafy than the grazing strains of the same variety. Some varieties also have dual purpose strains which are suitable for either grazing or cutting.

Apart from these differences in strain, varieties can also be classified as:

*Commercial strains.* These are very early to start growth in the spring; they flower early, and have the typical upright habit of growth of the hay strain. They do not live long, but may be useful in short leys.

*Pedigree strains.* These are strains which have been carefully selected and bred, and which will do well in most parts of the country. The S strains from Aberystwyth, and the new continental strains are good examples. Most of them are not so early in the spring as the commercial strains, but they are leafier and they live longer, and will normally grow better in the autumn.

### Grass Identification

Before it is possible to recognize plants in a grass field (see Table 9), it is necessary to know something about the parts which make up the plant.

VEGETATIVE (LEAFY) PARTS

*Stem*

(a) The *flowering stem* or *culm*. This grows erect and produces the flower. Most stems of annual grasses are culms.

(b) The *vegetative stem*. This does not produce a flower, and has not such an erect habit of growth as the culm. Perennial grasses have both flowering and vegetative stems.

*Leaves.* They are arranged on two alternate rows on the stem, and are attached to the stem at a node. Each leaf consists of two parts (see Fig. 38).

(a) The *sheath* which is attached to the stem.

(b) The *blade* which diverges from the stem.

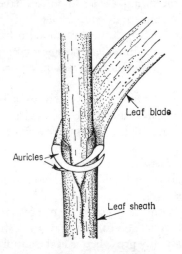

FIG. 38. Parts of the grass leaf.

The leaf sheath encloses the *buds* and *younger leaves*. Its edges may be *joined* (*entire*) or they may *overlap* each other (*split*) (see Fig. 39). If the leaves are *rolled* in the leaf sheath, the *shoots* will be *round* (see Fig. 40) but when *folded* the *shoots* will be *flattened* (see Fig. 41).

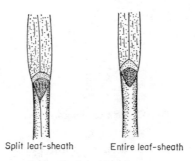

Split leaf-sheath          Entire leaf-sheath

Fɪɢ. 39. Parts of the grass leaf.

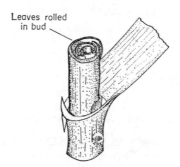

Leaves rolled
in bud

Fɪɢ. 40. Parts of the grass leaf.

Leaf folded
in the bud

Fɪɢ. 41. Parts of the grass leaf.

At the junction between the leaf blade and leaf sheath is the *ligule*. This is an outgrowth from the inner lining of the sheath (see Fig. 42).

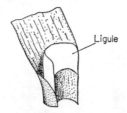

Ligule

FIG. 42. Parts of the grass leaf.

The *auricles* may also be seen on some grasses where the blade joins the sheath. They are a pair of clawlike outgrowths (see Fig. 38).

In some species, the leaf blade will show distinct veins when held against the light.

According to the variety, the underside of the leaf blade may be shiny or dull.

Other features of the leaves are more variable, and are not very reliable, and they can vary with age.

### INFLORESCENCE—THE FLOWER HEAD OF THE GRASS

The inflorescence consists of a number of branches called *spikelets* which carry the flowers. There are two types of inflorescence:

(1) The *spike*—the spikelets are attached to the main stem without a stalk (see Fig. 43).
(2) The *panicle*—the spikelets are attached to the main stem with a stalk (see Fig. 44). In some grasses the spikelets are attached to the main stem with very short stalks to form a dense type of inflorescence termed *spike-like* (see Fig. 45).

The spikelet is normally made up of an *axis*, bearing at its base the *upper* and *lower glumes* (see Fig. 46). Most grasses have two glumes.

A spike
inflorescence

Fɪɢ. 43. Grass inflorescence.

A panicle
Inflorescence

Fɪɢ. 44. Grass inflorescence.

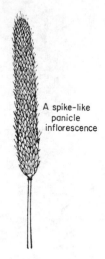

A spike-like
panicle
inflorescence

FIG. 45. Grass inflorescence.

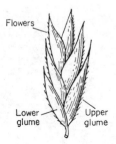

Flowers

Lower
glume

Upper
glume

FIG. 46. The spikelet.

Above the glumes, and arranged in the same way, are the *outer* and *inner pales*. In some species these pales may carry *awns* which are usually extensions from the pales (see Fig. 47).

Within the pales is the *flower*.

The flower consists of three parts (see Fig. 48).

(1) The male organs—*three stamens*.

(2) The female organ—the rounded *ovary* from which arise the feathery *stigmas*.

(3) A *pair* of *lodicules*—at the base of the ovary. They are indirectly concerned with the fertilization process, which is basically the same in all species of plants (see p. 23).

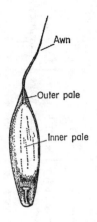

FIG. 47. The pales.

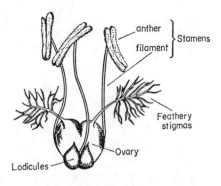

FIG. 48. The flower of the grass.

TABLE 9. HOW TO RECOGNIZE THE IMPORTANT GRASSES

| | Short duration ryegrasses | Perennial ryegrass | Meadow fescue | Cocksfoot | Timothy |
|---|---|---|---|---|---|
| Leaf sheath | Definitely split. Pink at base. Rolled in shoot. | Split or entire. Pink at base. Folded in shoot. | Split. Pink at base. Rolled in shoot. | Entire at first, later split. Folded in shoot. | Split. Pale at base. Rolled in shoot. |
| Blade | Broad. Margin smooth. Dark green. | Narrow. Margin smooth. Dark green. | Narrow. Margin rough. Lighter green. | Broad. Margin rough. Light green. | Broad. Margin smooth. Light green. |
| Lower side | Shiny. | Shiny. | Shiny. | Dull. | Dull. |
| Ligule | Blunt. | Short and blunt. | Small, blunt, greenish-white. | Long and transparent. | Prominent and membranous. |
| Auricles | Medium size and spreading. | Small, clasping the stem. | Small, narrow and spreading. | Absent. | Absent. |
| General | Veins indistinct when held to light. Not hairy. | Not hairy. | Veins appear as white lines when held to light. Not hairy. | Not hairy. | Base of shoots may be swollen. Not hairy. |

## Identification of the Legumes
See Table 10.

*Leaves*. With the exception of the first leaves (which may be simple) all leaves are compound. In some species the midrib is extended slightly to form a *mucronate* tip. Other features on the leaf may be *serrated* margins, presence or absence of marks, colour and

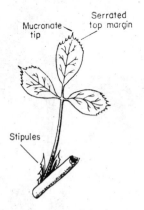

FIG. 49. Parts of the legume.

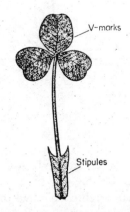

FIG. 50. Parts of the legume.

hairyness (see Figs. 49 and 50). The leaves are arranged alternately on the stem, and they can consist of the *stalk* which bears two or more leaflets according to the species (see Fig. 51).

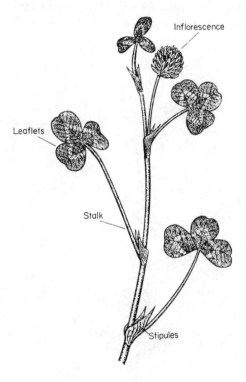

FIG. 51. Parts of the legume.

*Stipules.* These are attached to the base of the leaf stalk. They vary in shape and colour (see Fig. 50).

*Flower.* The flowers are brightly coloured, and being arranged on a central axis form an indefinite type of inflorescence (see p. 24).

TABLE 10. How to Recognize the Important Legumes

|  | Leaves, etc. | Stipule | General | Species |
|---|---|---|---|---|
| Mucronate tip | Centre leaflet with prominent stalk. Leaflets serrated at tip. | Broad, serrated and sharply pointed. | May be hairy. | **Lucerne.** |
|  | 6–12 pairs leaflets, plus a terminal one. | Thin, finely pointed. | Stems 1–2 ft high. Slightly hairy. | **Sainfoin.** |
| No mucronate tip | Trifoliate, dark green with white half-moon markings on upper surface. | Membranous with greenish purple veins. Pointed. | Hairy. | **Red clover.** |
|  | Trifoliate, serrated edge with or without markings on upper surface. | Small and pointed. | Not hairy. | **White clover.** |

## Some terms used in Grassland

Before discussing grasses and grassland management it is important to understand what is meant by the following terms:

*Seeding year:* the year in which the seeds mixture is sown.

*First harvest year:* the first year after the seeding year, and thus the second and third, etc., harvest years.

*Undersowing:* sowing the seeds mixture with another crop (a cover crop). It is usually a cereal crop.

*Direct sowing or seeding:* sowing on bare ground without a cover crop.

*Direct re-seeding* strictly means sowing without a cover crop, and putting the field straight back to grass, the previous crop having been grass. Very often it is used in the same way as direct sowing.

## Grasses

Over 150 different varieties of grasses can be found growing in this country, but only a few are of any importance to the farmer:

The short duration ryegrasses—this class consists of varieties which fall into three main groups: Westerwolths ryegrass, Italian ryegrass, and H.1 short rotation ryegrass.

Perennial ryegrass.

Cocksfoot.

Timothy.

Meadow fescue.

SHORT DURATION RYEGRASSES (see Fig. 52)

*Westerwolths.* This is an annual and the quickest growing of all grasses. A good crop can often be obtained within 6–8 weeks of sowing. It should not be undersown (see page 194), and is best direct sown (page 194) in the spring and summer as it is not at all winter hardy. Dutch bred varieties are used.

*Italian ryegrass.* This is short-lived (most varieties persist for 18–24 months); very quick to establish. Sown in the spring, Italian rye-

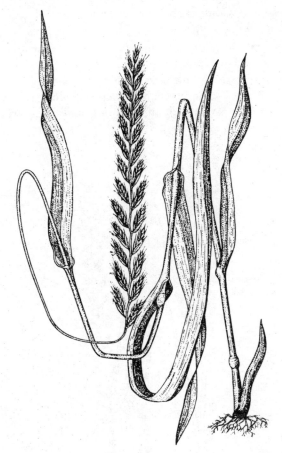

FIG. 52. Short duration ryegrass.

grass can produce good growth in its seeding year and an early bite
the following year, but for optimum production in its harvest year
(particularly the spring) it is best sown in summer or early autumn.
It does well under most conditions, but responds best to fertile
soils and plenty of nitrogen. Although stemmy it is palatable with a
high digestibility (see page 209).

R.v.P., Lema, Combita and Optima are continental varieties. They are all leafy and quite persistent.

*H.1 short rotation ryegrass.* Some strains in this group are similar to the more persistent Italian ryegrass strains and others are similar to perennial ryegrass, example Grasslands Manawa.

Sabrina a new Italian/perennial Ryegrass hybrid is a tetraploid (page 197) which is very early in the spring and it is also reasonably winter hardy.

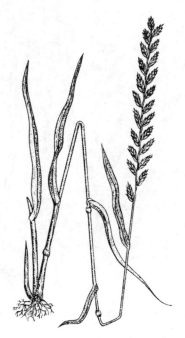

FIG. 53. Perennial ryegrass.

PERENNIAL RYEGRASS (see FIG. 53)

This forms the basis of the majority of long leys. The most important grass found in good permanent pastures. It is quick to establish, and yields well in the spring, early summer and autumn. It does best under fertile conditions, and responds well to nitrogen.

Perennial ryegrass is highly digestible.

Early and medium early varieties: S.24, Premo, Reveille (Tetraploid), Gremie.

Medium late varieties: S.101, Taptoe (Tetraploid), Talbot.

Late varieties: S.23, Semperweide, Endura.

### TETRAPLOID RYEGRASSES

The chromosome numbers in the cell nuclei have been doubled. The seeds are larger, and this will normally mean a slightly higher seed rate. They generally produce a bigger plant than the diploid (ordinary grass), but in yield of dry matter there is no great difference.

Most of the recommended tetraploids are from the Netherlands, and they do appear to have a better resistance to frost than the British diploids, but this is probably due to the country of origin.

Tetraploids are characteristically deep green, and are slightly more palatable and digestible than diploids. But because of their higher moisture content, tetraploids are perhaps not quite so suitable for conservation in the wetter parts of the country, particularly with high nitrogen use.

Sown alone they are not so persistent, as they tend to produce rather too open a sward.

### COCKSFOOT (see Fig. 54)

This is quick to establish, and is fairly early in the spring. It is the highest yielding of all grasses, but unless it is heavily stocked it will soon become coarse and unpalatable. It is one of the most deep-rooting of all grasses, and is therefore an excellent drought resister, and it does not need really fertile conditions. It should be considered as a special-purpose grass on the drier lighter soils in areas of low rainfall. It is not as digestible as the other important grasses.

Medium varieties: S.37, Roskilde Late, Modac.

Late varieties: S.26, Prairial.

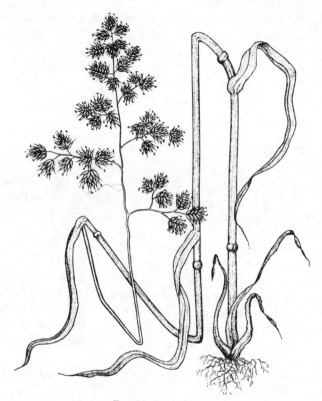

FIG. 54. Cocksfoot.

TIMOTHY (see Fig. 55).

This is fairly quick to establish. It is not particularly early in the spring. It is less productive than the other commonly used grasses, but is very palatable, although its digestibility is not as good as the ryegrasses. It is winter hardy, and does well under a wide range of conditions except on very light, dry soils.

Early and medium early varieties: S.352, Scots, Kampe 11.

Medium late varieties: S.51, Pecora.

Late varieties: S.48, Oakmere, Inkenso.

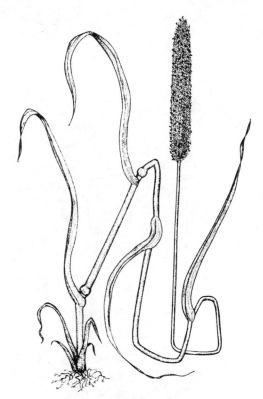

Fig. 55. Timothy.

MEADOW FESCUE (see Fig. 56)

This is rather slow to establish, but once established it is very productive. It is fairly early in the spring. It does very well when sown in conjunction with timothy. Meadow fescue shows high digestibility.

Early varieties: Comtessa, Rossa.
Late varieties: Bundy, Sceempter Pasture.

See N.I.A.B. leaflet No. 16 for further details of grasses.

Fig. 56. Meadow fescue.

## Other Grasses

TALL FESCUE

Once it is well established, strains such as S 170 are extremely useful for early grass in the spring, and being very hardy it can also be grazed in the winter.

RED FESCUE AND SHEEP'S FESCUE

Both are small plants which are only suitable for poor upland and marginal soils. They are more productive under these conditions than the better known grasses.

ROUGH AND SMOOTH STALKED MEADOW GRASS, AND
CRESTED DOG'S TAIL

These used to be included in seeds mixtures. They are not, however, very productive, and are too expensive to consider these days.

GRASSES IN THE FUTURE

High energy (high percentage of carbohydrate) *ryegrasses* are being developed by plant breeders at Aberystwyth. Potentially these have much higher yielding capabilities than the grasses at present grown. A *tall fescue/perennial ryegrass* hybrid has also been developed, and if it can be grown for commercial use this could mean an extension of both ends of the grazing season. A *meadow fescue/perennial ryegrass* cross shows promise. This should combine the winter hardiness of the fescue and the quick growth of the ryegrass. And finally there are indications of a new *Cocksfoot* with a digestibility as high as the ryegrasses. This would be an extremely valuable variety on light, dry soils.

WEED GRASSES

The majority of grasses naturally growing in this country are of little value. But some of them are extremely persistent and are able to grow under very poor conditions where the more valuable grasses would not thrive. However, their production is always low, they are usually unpalatable, and under most conditions they can be considered as weeds.

Well-known examples of weed grasses are:

*The bents.* They are very unproductive and unpalatable and are found in poor permanent pastures.

*Brome grasses.* They are found in arable fields and also in short leys. There are many species, and none are of any value.

*Yorkshire fog.* This is extremely unpalatable except when very young. It is prevalent under acid conditions, although it can be found growing almost anywhere. It is sometimes used in reclaiming hill pastures.

## Clovers

Clovers are essential plants for the longer ley and permanent pasture. In the short ley they are used for conservation. Apart from their ability to fix nitrogen from the atmosphere, clovers are also useful in that, especially in the longer ley, they act as "bottom plants". With their creeping habit of growth they knit the sward together and help to keep out weeds. Although the majority of clovers are palatable with a high feeding value and digestibility (particularly white clover), they are not so productive as the grasses, and they must not be allowed to dominate the sward at the expense of the grasses. The clovers of agricultural importance are the red and white clovers.

### RED CLOVERS (see Fig. 57)

These are short lived. They are included in short leys and sometimes in long leys to improve bulk in the early years. Although used more for conservation, some of the more persistent improved strains are useful for grazing. There are three types.

*Broad red clovers.* The newer varieties, particularly the tetraploids such as Hungaropoly and Teroba, are far more persistent and higher yielding than the older English varieties. They also show high resistance to clover rot.

Sabtoron, a new diploid from Aberystwyth, is quite persistent, and has a good resistance to stem eelworm.

*Single cut red clovers* are later in growth and to flower in the spring than the Broad red varieties. S.151 is the earliest of this group, and it will certainly last two harvest years.

*Late flowering red clovers.* These varieties last longer than the broad red clovers. Under good conditions they persist for at least 3 years. They also stand up to grazing better than the other red clovers. S 123 can persist up to 4 years.

FIG. 57. Red clover.

WHITE CLOVERS (see Fig. 58)

These should be regarded as the foundation of the grazing ley. They are generally not so productive as the red clovers, but are more persistent. There are three types.

*Medium-large leaved white clovers.* These varieties are becoming more popular because of their ability to compete better with the heavy nitrogen use on grazing leys. Kersey is a very productive variety, whilst Blanco R.v.P. appears to tolerate quite high rates of nitrogen fertilizer. Sabeda does well in the west of the country, although it is not resistant to clover rot.

*Medium-small leaved white clovers.* These are extremely useful in leys of up to 4 years and are very quick to establish. S 100 is the best-known variety.

FIG. 58. White clover.

*Small leaved white clovers.* These are the most essential of all plants in the long ley. They are rather slow to establish but can become dominant. Kent wild white clover is a good local variety and S184 is another very productive and creeping type.

See N.I.A.B. leaflet No. 4 for further details of clovers.

## Other Legumes

LUCERNE (see Fig. 59)

This is a very deep-rooting legume and it is therefore useful on dry soils, although it can be grown successfully under a wide range of soil conditions provided drainage is good. For better establishment lucerne should be grown with a companion grass such as cocksfoot, timothy or meadow fescue. Although it is very productive lucerne is not very palatable and it is the least digestible of all the important legumes. It is probably best utilized by drying through the grass drier, although excellent barn dried lucerne hay can be made without much loss of leaf. There are many varieties of lucerne, and in this country they can be grouped into early and mid-season types. Where possible the early type should be grown.

FIG. 59. Lucerne.

At present *Europe* is the heaviest yielding variety, but where verticilium wilt is suspected, *Vertus* is worth considering.

SAINFOIN (See Fig. 60)

As regards its economic use, sainfoin is very similar to lucerne although it is not so productive. It has not been very popular in the past, due to difficulties in establishment (it does not compete very well with weeds), but sown with grasses such as cocksfoot, this problem has been overcome. For forage purposes especially it should be seriously considered for calcareous soils. Sainfoin hay is highly valued for horses, but it is difficult to make without losing leaf. There are two major types of sainfoin.

*French or giant.* This is heavy yielding, but short-lived.

FIG. 60. Sainfoin.

*Common or Old English.* This lasts for several years, but is not so heavy yielding.

See N.I.A.B. leaflet No. 4 for further information on lucerne and sainfoin.

### Herbs

These are deep-rooting plants which are generally beneficial to pastures. But to be of any value, they should be palatable, in no way harmful to stock, and they should not compete with other species in the sward. They have a high mineral content which may benefit the grazing animal.

Yarrow, chicory, rib grass and burnet (see Figs. 61–64) are the most useful of the many herbs which exist. They can be included

FIG. 61. Yarrow.

FIG. 62. Chicory.

FIG. 63. Rib grass.

in seeds mixture for a grazing type of long ley. They are not cheap, however, and as one or more of these herbs will usually get into the sward on its own accord, there does not seem much point in buying them in the first place.

## Herbage Digestibility

One of the main characteristics which determine the feeding value of herbage plants is its digestibility, i.e. the amount of the plant which is actually digested by the animal. Until recently, the digestibility of foods was only determined by animal feeding experiments. But, with the development of the laboratory *in vitro* technique which simulates rumen digestion, it is now possible for the digestibility of any species of herbage plant to be assessed very much more easily without using animals.

The digestibility of herbage plants is now expressed as the D value *which is the percentage of digestible organic matter in the dry matter.*

High digestibility values are desirable as it means that the animal is able to obtain the greatest amount of nutrients from the herbage being fed.

D value will vary according to species, variety and management, notably stage of growth for grazing or cutting. And once the maximum D value has been reached, unless the plant is defoliated it falls quite quickly depending on the species or variety.

With *grasses*, for conditions approximating to *grazing*, the D value for perennial ryegrass is about 70%, but for cocksfoot it is approximately 66%. Short duration ryegrass and meadow fescue have D values just below 70% with timothy at about 68%. For *conservation*, higher yields will result when the crop is cut at a later stage of growth, but on average the D value is 7% lower in all the varieties mentioned.

With *legumes*, white clover has a higher D value (about 75%) than the grasses, and it does maintain its maximum value over a longer period. For these reasons alone it should be seriously considered in grazing leys of three or more years' duration even with high nitrogen use. Sainfoin has a D value of about 65%; red clover and lucerne are approximately 62%. Lucerne over the season will show a higher yield of digestible dry matter than the other legumes, especially if when made into hay, the loss of leaf is kept to a minimum.

Fig. 64. Burnet.

### Seeds Mixtures

Many farmers depend on reliable seeds firms to supply them with standard seeds mixtures, whilst others prefer to plan their own mixtures which the merchant will then make up for them.

The following points must be considered when deciding upon a seeds mixture.

## THE PURPOSE OF THE LEY

Varieties and strains of herbage plants have different growth characteristics, and because of this the type of stock using the ley will, influence the choice of seed. This is shown in Table 11.

TABLE 11

| Purpose | Varieties which should be used |
|---|---|
| For early grazing in the spring, i.e. early bite. | Mainly ryegrass or possibly tall fescue. |
| For an attempted even balance of production throughout the season. | Ryegrass and non-ryegrass. |
| For winter grazing cattle— foggage (provided conditions allow). | Cocksfoot and timothy. |
| For the grazing animal only (particularly sheep). | Strains of grasses which produce a closely knit sward. |
| For conservation only (silage and hay). | Strains of grasses which produce a tall habit of growth. |

## SOIL AND CLIMATIC CONDITIONS

Most strains of grasses and legumes will grow where there is a reasonable amount of rainfall, but in dry conditions deep-rooting and therefore drought resistant plants, such as cocksfoot, lucerne, and sainfoin are advisable. On heavy, wet soils there is no point in growing early grasses or planning for foggage grazing. Like the majority of crops, grasses and particularly legumes will not thrive where there is a lack of lime in the soil.

THE LENGTH OF THE LEY

Perennial ryegrass, cocksfoot, timothy and meadow fescue, being persistent, are suitable for long leys, whilst the less persistent and quick-growing early types, of which Italian ryegrass is an outstanding example, will make up the short ley.

COST OF THE MIXTURE

This will vary from season to season depending upon the previous year's seed harvest, the strain of plant used and the seed rate. It is false economy to buy unsuitable strains just because they are cheap. It is equally unwise to be persuaded to buy expensive and often unproved seed. Generally speaking, it will be found that varieties required for the short term ley are cheaper than those for the longer ley.

Tables 12–14 give examples of different seeds mixtures.

### Making a New Ley

A case can be made for sowing the seeds either in the spring or late summer/early autumn period.

SPRING SOWING

If direct sowing without a cover crop, the maiden seeds can give valuable production in the summer. Establishment can be enhanced by stock being able to graze the developing sward within a few weeks of sowing. This is not possible to the same extent with autumn sowing. A limiting factor with spring sowing may be moisture, and in the drier districts, the seeds should be sown at the beginning of March if possible. The plant should thus establish itself sufficiently well to withstand a probable dry period in late spring. Of course, undersowing in corn (which is only possible in the spring) does mean that the fullest possible use is being made of the field, although with the slower growing grasses, establishment is usually not so good.

Table 12. 1-Year Leys (Amounts in kg/ha or lb/acre).

| | Westerwolths | I.R.G. | Broad red clover | Late flowering red clover | Total | |
|---|---|---|---|---|---|---|
| A | 25–30 | | | | 25–30 | Not suitable for undersowing; extremely quick to establish; will produce two good cuts or grazings, especially if the first one is taken before the seeds are set. |
| B | | 20–40 R.V.P. | | | 20–40 | The lower seed rate is used in the wetter parts of the country. Stemmy but palatable. Chiefly used for grazing. |
| C | | 15 R.V.P.<br>15 Optima | | | 30 | Becoming quite popular; for general use, although chiefly for grazing. |
| D | | 16 Optima | 6 tetraploid | | 22 | When undersown will give autumn grazing; in the following year two good crops, usually, but not always, for conservation. |
| E | | 16 Optima | 4 tetraploid | 3S:123 | 23 | Very similar to mixture D—but will give better aftermath grazing because of the inclusion of the L.F.R.C. |

In the examples given ryegrass is the only variety of grass used. The emphasis must be on quick establishment with good production from an early stage, and with an ability to respond well to nitrogen. As persistency is not important, the short duration ryegrasses will amply fulfil these requirements, provided that management is correct.

TABLE 13. 2–4-YEAR LEYS (Amounts in kg/ha or lb/acre)

| | Short duration ryegrass (not, Westerwolths) | Perennial ryegrass | Cocksfoot | Timothy | Meadow fescue | Broad red clover | Late flowering red clover | White clover | Total | |
|---|---|---|---|---|---|---|---|---|---|---|
| A | 4 | 12 S 24 | | | | 2 tetra-ploid | 3 S 123 | 1 S 100 | 22 | This mixture should give early bite, an extremely useful hay or silage crop, and good aftermath grazing, but plenty of nitrogen will be needed for maximum production. If S 24 is replaced by S 101 the ley should last 4 years. |
| B | 20 Optima | | | | | | | 2 S 100 | 22 | A mixture which should quite easily last 3 years, but if growing conditions are not ideal, replace 10 kg of Optima with 10 kg of S 23. This is an easy ley to manage, and can be extremely productive when liberally fed with nitrogen. |
| C | 20 R.v.P. | 10 S 24 | | | | | | | 30 | A very productive ley. With no clover to depress, up to 375 kg/ha (300 units/acre) of nitrogen can be economically applied in the season. |
| D | | | | 8 S 48 | 10 Bundy | | | 2 S 100 | 20 | More of a grazing mixture. Not early in the spring, but should give even production throughout the season with good late grazing. This mixture would not do so well on lighter soils, but if, say 5 kg Prairial cocksfoot were added it would be more productive under those conditions. |
| E | 4 | | 14 S 37 | | | | 3 S 123 | 1 S 100 | 22 | For really poor soil types this mixture would be suitable for general purpose use. |

TABLE 14. LONG LEYS (Amounts in kg/ha or lb/acre)

| | Perennial ryegrass | Cocksfoot | Timothy | Meadow fescue | Late flowering red S 123 clover | White clover | Wild white clover | Total | |
|---|---|---|---|---|---|---|---|---|---|
| A | 20 S 23 | | | | | 2 S 100 | ½ S 184 | 22½ | For general purpose use. A very productive and hard-wearing ley. |
| B | | | 8 S 48 | 10 S 215 | | 2 S 100 | ½ S 184 | 20½ | For general purpose use. This ley will tie in well with the previous ryegrass mixture, and by managing the two leys together it should be possible to get fairly even production throughout the season. |
| C | | 5 S 26<br>5 S 37<br>5 Prairial | | | | 2 S 100 | ½ S 184 | 17½ | This mixture could be managed in a similar way as B, but is suited to the lighter, poorer soils. |
| D | 13 S 101 | 7 S 26 | 4 S 48 | | 3 S 123 | 1 S 100 | ½ S 184 | 28½ | This is the famous Cockle Park type general purpose mixture. It is meant to give even production throughout the whole season, but eventually, depending upon the soil type and management, it will tend to become either ryegrass or cocksfoot dominant. |

It will be noted that wild white clover is included in these mixtures. After about 3 years it should have established itself sufficiently well to fill in the bottom of the ley and give a nice well-knit sward. Only a small amount is needed, otherwise it will tend to dominate the whole sward at the expense of the more productive grasses.

LATE SUMMER/EARLY AUTUMN SOWING

There is usually some rain at this time; heavy dews have started again, and the soil is warm. But with clovers in the seeds mixture earlier sowing may have to be carried out so that the plants have developed a good tap root system before the onset of frosts. Earlier sowing is not always possible.

UNDERSOWING OR DIRECT SOWING

There are points for and against either of the practices, but in general undersowing is more popular. However, where conditions are not so good, and where extra grass is required in the summer, direct sowing is preferable. But with short leys, undersowing is more normally carried out.

Green crops as cover crops are excellent, e.g.

(1) Rape sown at 4·5–7 kg/ha (4–6 lb/acre) with the seeds mixture, and grazed off in 6–10 weeks.

(2) Oats or barley sown at 63 kg/ha (56 lb/acre) with the seeds mixture.

(3) Oats or barley as whole crop silage which is cut at the end of June.

## Sowing the Crop

DIRECT SOWING

Reference has already been made to the cultivations necessary for preparing the right sort of seed-bed for the seeds (see p. 79). But it must be re-emphasized that grass and clover seeds are small, and therefore they must be sown shallow, and that therefore a fine and firm seed-bed is necessary.

With ample moisture the seed can be broadcast. This should be on a ribbed-rolled surface, so that the seeds tend to fall into the small furrows made by the roller. Most fertilizer distributors can be used for broadcasting, or for smaller acreages, the shandy barrow is still very useful.

In the drier areas, and on lighter soils, drilling is safer. The seed is then in much closer contact with the soil. The 10 cm (4 in.) coulter spacing of the ordinary grass drill should give a satisfactory cover of seeds, but if using the corn drill with 18 cm (7 in.) spacing, the seeds should be cross-drilled. After either broadcasting or drilling, except on the wetter seed-beds (when the seeds harrow will be used), rolling will complete the whole operation. Where necessary, 375 kg/ha (3 cwt/acre) of a compound fertilizer e.g. (12:12:18) can be broadcast and worked in during the final seed-bed preparations, or, depending on the drill used, it can be applied with the seed.

### UNDERSOWING

Any of the *autumn-sown* cereals may be used as a cover crop but they compete more with the seeds than spring sown cereals. Harrowing of the ground will be necessary, and then the seed should preferably be drilled across the corn drills followed by the light harrows. Alternatively, the seed can be broadcast and harrowed in, but this is not so satisfactory.

With a *spring sown* cover crop the cereal is sown first and it can be immediately followed by the seeds mixture drilled or broadcast. This is desirable with slow establishing mixtures but with vigorous species, e.g. Italian ryegrass and red clover it may be preferable to broadcast the seed after the cereal is established.

## Manuring of Grassland

Grass, like all crops, needs plant food for its establishment, maintenance and production. *Nitrogen* is essential for maximum production from grass. How much to apply will depend, to a certain extent, on the composition of the sward. Too much nitrogen, especially if the resulting sward is not properly utilized, can certainly check the clover. With a straight grass mixture (especially ryegrass) up to 440 kg/ha (350 units/acre) of nitrogen is normally justified in the year, provided other plant foods are in adequate supply. But the amount of nitrogen applied will often depend on the intensity of management.

It would be very unwise to apply all the nitrogen needed by the ley for the year in one application. Most of it would be wasted. It should be applied "little and often" from early February to October if necessary, depending upon the swards. It is important to use nitrogen, not only during natural periods of growth, i.e. spring and early autumn, but also to try and force production at other times of the season. See also Table 7 (page 93).

*Phosphate* and *potash* will both help in the establishment of the sward, and on most soils they are important in helping to maintain the general vigour and well-being of the ley. There is no doubt that the response to nitrogen by the grass crop is far greater if there is an adequate supply of phosphate and potash present.

*Phosphate* can be applied at any time of the year, though it is not really advisable during the winter non-growing period. Depending on the phosphorus index, but on the majority of soils, 38 kg/ha (30 units/acre) $P_2O_5$ is normally sufficient whether the crop is grazed or cut.

*Potash* should not be applied in the spring. The uptake of magnesium by the plant is always slow at that time of the year, and as potash tends to act as a buffer against magnesium, a spring application will accentuate a shortage of magnesium in the plant. This could well lead to hypomagnesaemia or grass staggers in the animal.

*For grazing swards,* depending on the potash status of the soil, 38 kg/ha (30 units/acre) or even less can be applied in the summer or autumn. The grazing animal itself recirculates potash back to the soil, and at normal stocking rates this can amount to more than 125 kg/ha (100 units/acre) in the year. If the soils annual natural contribution (63–250 kg/ha, depending on soil type) is added, it will be seen that it is not always necessary to apply potash. Luxury uptake of potash (the plant containing potash surplus to its needs) should be avoided. It is wasteful, and it does increase the risk of hypomagnesaemia.

*The cut crop* needs more potash than the grazed sward. A vigorous growing crop will take up about 357 kg/ha (300 units/acre) in the year. Depending upon soil type, up to 300 kg/ha (250 units/acre) could be needed to replace that removed. For efficient utilization, it should be applied at intervals through the season *after* the crop has been taken.

*Lime.* The grass, or grass/clover sward like any other crop cannot thrive in acid conditions. The legumes, particularly red clover and lucerne are very sensitive to a low pH (page 62). Maintenance dressings of up to 4 tonne/ha (1½ tons/acre) calcium carbonate are very often necessary for the crop.

## The Management of a Young Ley

### A DIRECT-SOWN LONG LEY IN ITS SEEDING YEAR—SOWN IN THE SPRING

The sward should be grazed 6–10 weeks after sowing, depending upon weather conditions which naturally affect growth. This early grazing helps to consolidate the developing sward, and encourages the plant to tiller out. It should not be too hard, but equally it is important not to undergraze. The sward should then be rested, and followed by periodic grazings throughout the season.

It is unwise to cut the ley in its seeding year. Plants which are allowed to grow too tall before being cropped never develop very strongly. The essential tillering is not encouraged to the same extent, and the sward is left "very open" into which weeds may soon gain a foothold.

If grazing is not possible, the plants should be topped before they grow too tall.

### A DIRECT-SOWN LEY—SOWN IN THE LATE SUMMER

This should either be grazed or topped in the autumn.

### AN UNDERSOWN LEY

This should either be grazed or topped in the autumn. If the seeds look "thin" after the corn has been harvested, 37 kg/ha (30 units/acre) of nitrogen will help to stimulate growth.

## Management of the Established Ley

*The ryegrasses* now make up more than 80% of the grass species used in leys.

With suitable fertilizer treatment, the late varieties of perennial ryegrass will now grow quite well in July and August, although this will depend on the season. This contrasts with previous years when in order to obtain a fairly uniform supply of grass throughout the growing period, non-ryegrass swards were managed alongside ryegrass mixtures. But as perennial ryegrass under most management conditions is the most productive grass, it is obviously sensible to use it wherever possible. However new and more productive *non-ryegrass* varieties and the introduction of hybrids (page 201) could change the picture in the future. There are still many farmers who will use a timothy/meadow fescue mixture as an insurance against poor production of the ryegrass. Non-ryegrass swards are also useful for winter grazing (foggage).

Tables 15 and 16 show ways of managing grassland. Naturally there will have to be modifications according to the season, growth and type of stock available. The management chiefly refers to the dairy cow, although some intensive beef grazing systems can also apply.

Management for other stock is referred to on page 226.

## Grazing by Stock

All stock do not graze in the same way. Some are much better grazers than others. The most efficient are store cattle, followed by dairy cows and fattening cattle, sheep and young cattle. Horses are notoriously bad grazers!

Mixed stocking is ideal. In this way fairly good utilization of the sward is achieved because what is not eaten by one class of stock will probably be consumed by other classes of stock. Mixed stocking is not always possible. But what should be done is to see that the most profitable stock get the best. This usually means the dairy cow or fattening beast, and at certain times of the year, the sheep flock.

TABLE 15. MANAGEMENT OF LONG LEYS

| | Jan. | Feb. | Mar. | April | May | June | July | Aug. | Sept. | Oct. | Nov. | Dec. |
|---|---|---|---|---|---|---|---|---|---|---|---|---|
| **Production** — Ryegrass leys | | | | | | | | | | | | |
| **Production** — Non-ryegrass leys | | | | | | | | | | | | |

**Manuring — Ryegrass leys**

Apply 75 kg/ha (60 units N/acre) to sheltered early fields for first bite.

(1) First bite taken.
(2) 50–75 kg/ha (40–60 units/acre) applied after grazing.
(3) Graze at intervals (normally 21–28 days) throughout the summer.
(4) Additional nitrogen is usually applied at 50–75 kg/ha (40–60 units/acre) a time after every crop is taken.
(5) Reasonably heavy grazing can be continued fairly late in the year to check the grasses and encourage the clovers.

(1) Apply 38 kg/ha (30 units/acre) $P_2O_5$ and 0–38 kg/ha (0–30 units/acre) $K_2O$ annually: 1–1·2 tonnes/ha (8–10 cwt/acre) of K slag (or the equivalent as ground mineral phosphate) can be used every 4–5 years. Do not graze stock after slag application until it is well washed in.
(2) For first bite, shut the field up after fertilizer application.
(3) Lime, if required.

**Management and — Non-ryegrass leys**

Foggage taken from well-drained dry fields.

(1) 50–75 kg/ha (40–60 units N/acre) applied.
(2) Graze at intervals throughout summer period, if possible taking any surplus for conservation.
(3) Additional nitrogen is normally applied at 50 kg/ha (40 units/acre) after every crop is taken.

(1) Apply 50 kg/ha (40 units/acre) nitrogen, 38 kg/ha (30 units/acre) $P_2O_5$ and 0–38 kg/ha (0–30 units/acre) $K_2O$ annually; 1–1·2 tonnes/ha (8–10 cwt/acre) of K slag (or ground mineral phosphate equivalent) can be used every 4–5 years. Do not graze stock until slag has been well washed in.
(2) If necessary, shut the ley up after fertilizer application for foggage grazing late in the winter (if conditions permit).
(3) Lime, if required.

This type of programme on these special purpose leys can be followed every year, modifying it according to season, state of the sward and the needs of the stock. In some years grazing should not be so intensive, and more conservation can be taken, and grazing should be finished earlier. All this will tend to check the clovers, and encourage the grasses. Thus it is a fairly easy matter to maintain a reasonably correct balance between the clovers and the grasses. Too much clover in the sward should be avoided, although too little clover will lead to an unproductive ley.

TABLE 16. MANAGEMENT OF SHORT LEYS

| | Seeding year | First year | Second year | |
|---|---|---|---|---|
| 1-year ley | After the cover crop has been removed, 37 kg/ha (30 units/acre) N can be applied to give useful grazing in September and October. Apply 50 kg/ha (40 units/acre) of $P_2O_5$ and $K_2O$ after this grazing. | If early bite is required, 75 kg/ha (60 units/acre) N, applied in February. Following early bite, 60 units N can be applied for conservation, followed by a further 60 units N for a second cut or graze. | | Lime should not be necessary. If possible, the arable break in the rotation should receive the lime. Rolling will probably be necessary in early spring as the leys are usually cut, and it is wise to press the stones down firmly. |
| 2-year ley | As for the 1-year ley. | As for the 1-year ley, with the addition of 37 kg/ha (40 units/acre) $P_2O_5$ and up to 120 kg/ha (150 units/acre) $K_2O$ in the autumn. | As for the previous year, except that the autumn application of $P_2O_5$ and $K_2O$ will not be needed. | |

INTENSIVE GRAZING

The introduction of the electric fence brought about one of the greatest revolutions in grassland farming. By its use controlled grazing is possible.

There are basically two methods of controlled grazing.

(1) *Paddock grazing* (Fig. 65). The basic principle of the paddock system is rotational grazing alternating with rest periods. The grazing area is divided into equal sized paddocks which will normally occupy the fields near the milking unit where access is easy. On average grass requires about 3 weeks to reach the grazing stage, and assuming that each paddock is grazed for 1 day, 21 paddocks are needed to provide the rotation. The size of each paddock will depend on the number of cows in the herd and the duration of grazing. Depending on management (including fertilizer treatment), when the sward is growing well, and at about 150 mm (6 in.) high, 100 cows will need about 0·8 *hectares* (50 cows/acre) per day of fresh grass. Certainly 0·2 hectares (half an acre) of grass should provide sufficient grazing for a dairy cow from April to September. Thus on this basis, as an example, 20 hectares (50 acres) divided into 21 one-day paddocks, will be needed for a 100-cow herd.

At the peak of spring growth it may be possible to alternate round less of the paddocks in which case any surplus grass should, if possible, be cut for silage or even hay. Naturally, adjustments will have to be made, when the crop is not so productive, with other grass brought into the system.

With the paddock system it is preferable if the paddocks are kept separate from the conservation area. Management is easier and different types of swards can be grown to suit the different methods of utilization (see Table 15).

*Note:* The Wye College system of grazing comprises four plots each of which is divided into seven sub-plots, a fresh one being grazed daily. This gives a 28-day grazing cycle.

Other grazing systems have also been evolved.

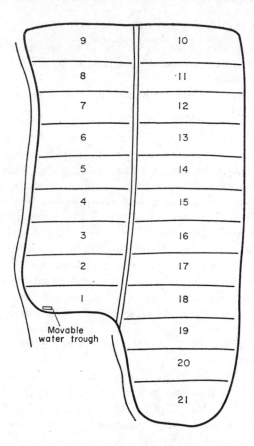

FIG. 65. Paddock grazing.

(2) *Strip grazing* (Fig. 66). This is particularly suitable for the dairy cow, whereby the animal is allowed access to a limited area of fresh crop either twice daily, daily, or for longer intervals. It is certainly the most efficient form of grazing especially for the smaller herd. If no other stock are following on behind the cows, the back fence should be used, whereby the area once grazed is

almost immediately fenced off. This is to protect the recovering sward from constantly being nibbled over. Without the back fence the recovery rate is very much slower.

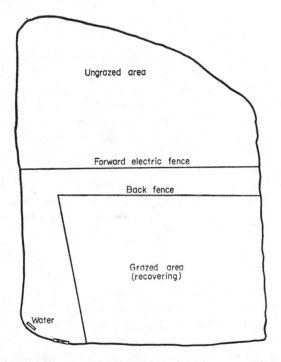

Ungrazed area

Forward electric fence

Back fence

Grazed area
(recovering)

Water

FIG. 66. Strip grazing.

Whatever method of grazing, the yardstick must be the production and condition of the stock, coupled as far as possible with the condition of the sward, although too much emphasis should not be placed on this second point. Given a reasonable rest period, a good ley will soon recover, but the mower may have to be used to top-over the uneven effects of grazing. However, with a well-run paddock system this should not often be necessary, especially in the wetter areas.

With any system of grazing, if grass surplus to the requirements of the stock is taken for conservation, extra potash (usually 50 kg/ha) (40 units/acre) should be applied *after* the crop has been taken.

### FOLLOWING STOCK

Followers can be fitted in behind the strip-grazed dairy cow or fattening beast to graze extensively, but it will not, of course, be practicable with the paddock system. In fact with whatever method of grazing, management is often easier if followers are kept separate, and it is an increasing practice to keep some leys exclusively for intensive milk or meat production, and other pastures (sometimes permanent pastures) are kept for the followers. Calves should, as far as possible, be grazed on new swards.

A good permanent pasture can of course be managed in exactly the same way as the established ley. There is in fact now sufficient evidence to show that given the same treatment, a good permanent pasture is more productive than a ley.

### GRAZING SYSTEMS FOR OTHER STOCK
*Beef Cattle—Summer fattening of Strong Stores*

(a) *Paddock grazing.* Modern systems of paddock-grazing for beef cattle normally involves dividing the grazing area into, at the most, ten paddocks, grazing each in turn for a maximum of three days. Stocking rates in the spring at 6 head/ha (2½ head/acre) demands, especially in the wetter areas, up to 250 kg/ha (200 units/acre) nitrogen, commencing with 25 kg/ha (20 units/acre) in the spring, and about 62 kg/ha (50 units/acre) after every other graze with more, 37·5 kg/ha (30 units/acre), being added if grass in a particular paddock is conserved.

(b) *Traditional.* The majority of farmers prefer to fatten their beasts more extensively. The management is quite different. Usually the stock are turned into the field at the beginning of the grazing season, and are kept there all the time. 75 kg/ha (60 units/acre) nitrogen is normally applied in early spring. For finishing, a stocking rate of 2½ bullocks/ha (1 bullock/acre) is usual, and they should be able to put on a liveweight increase of 100 kg (2 cwt) in the season May till July. The field then takes a second group of cattle although they can never be finished off without supplementary feeding.

Good permanent pastures are generally preferred by the fattener. There is something in a permanent pasture (and it is hard to explain what it is!) which finishes off a beast that much better compared with most leys.

With permanent pasture, particularly, the farmer will usually know its capabilities throughout the season. He will be able to adjust the stocking according to previous experience, and also, of course, by the appearance of the stock. Rate of growth will, to a certain extent, depend upon the type of season.

## The Semi-intensive System

Paddock-grazing with beef is seen at its best for this system. It can be run on more flexible lines as the stock are not being finished at grass, although a high daily liveweight gain is essential.

The paddocks are normally grazed continuously until about the end of June, and then the stock are moved onto the silage aftermath. The hitherto grazed area is put up for conservation, and when this has been cut, the stock, at what will then be at the end of the season, graze the whole area. Stocking rates at about 11 to the hectare (4½–5 to the acre) will be higher at the start of the season, but the increase in weight and appetite of the stock coincides with a fall in production from the grass as the season continues. This should mean a reduction in stocking rate to about 6/ha (2½/acre) and then about 4/ha (1·5/acre). Liveweight gains of 3·3–3·75 kg (1·5–1·7 lb) per day should be obtained. Up to 312 kg/ha (250 units/acre) nitrogen are used in the season.

Although this system is normally associated with paddocks, set-stocking (whereby the field to be grazed is treated as one whole area) is now becoming popular again. Less labour is needed as the cattle do not have to be moved every few days, and fencing costs are less. Liveweight gains can show a marginal improvement compared with paddock grazing.

GRAZING WITH SHEEP

For quite a large part of the year the grass sheep flock should be regarded as a scavenger flock. There is no reason to treat them otherwise.

It is impossible to give any hard and fast rules on the rates of stocking. The grass will obviously not be at its best, as other stock would have already been over it. The sheep are simply clearing up. Therefore the condition of the stock must be watched and stocking rates adjusted accordingly. But do not overgraze the pasture with sheep.

Better grass is needed for ewes being flushed, and for ewes and lambs for fat lamb production.


GRAZING SYSTEMS

There are three main methods of grazing management for the ewes and their lambs during the fattening period.

(1) *Set-stocking* is the least complicated of any form of fat lamb production off grass and properly managed it can produce the quickest grown early lamb, probably because of lack of disturbance for the flock. The stocking rate is normally at about 8·5 ewes/ha (3–4 ewes/acre) and lambs on average land and grass. The development of new anthelmintics has meant that worm infestation with set stocking is not now such a serious risk.

(2) *Rotational grazing:* Where the ewes (stocking rate 10 ewes/ha) (4 ewes/acre) and lambs move round a number of fields or paddocks in sequence. Usually three or four paddocks are involved, and the flock completes the rotation in about three weeks.

Provided the flock has clean feet to start with, the organism responsible for foot rot will be kept in check by rotational grazing, although this is not the case with parasitic worms. There will certainly be a better kill of larvae if each paddock is rigorously defoliated by the stock. However this will increase the competition for grass for the lamb from the ewe, and so its progress will be checked.

(3) *Forward creep grazing.* With this system the lambs have access

to unlimited supplies of fresh grass without competition from the ewes. Good performances have been recorded of liveweight gains of the lambs, and coupled with the heavy stocking rates possible (up to 25 ewes and their lambs to the hectare (10 ewes to the acre)). this type of intensive management (in terms of performance per hectare) of sheep on leys can be considered. However more fencing is needed (6 paddocks are involved in a 21–24-day cycle) and neither early nor young fat lambs are produced.

Provided the flock starts off clean, there need not be a build-up of parasitic worm infection.

Grass for any system of fat lamb production needs nitrogen; 75–125 kg/ha (60–100 units/acre) can be applied at the start of the season, but the season and growth will dictate if more nitrogen is applied later in the year.

**Zero grazing** or the feeding of fresh cut grass to stock is an old practice. It used to be called green soiling, then being associated with a much wider range of crops than is the case these days. Grass or grass/clover mixtures are now mainly used, although the future could well see other crops being grown again.

There are various reasons for the revival of interest in the technique. When maximum stocking rate has been achieved by orthodox grazing, zero-grazing, in most situations can increase stocking intensity by 5–10%. But it is a twice a day all the season operation involving expensive machinery which of necessity must be extremely reliable. In addition there is the problem of dealing with the slurry from stock housed all the year round. Overall extra costs incurred could amount to about £6·00 per cow per year.

### The Improvement of Pastures

Poor permanent pasture can be recognized by a mat of old decaying vegetation at the bottom of the sward. This is usually the result of poor management over a long period, such as bad grazing and not enough fertilizer. The better plants are choked out, and inferior grasses such as the bents are encouraged. The cheapest, simplest and quickest way of improving an old pasture is to plough it up and direct re-seed it. This is not always possible, and so the mat must be destroyed in other ways. Until recently, pasture improvement (other than ploughing) was a slow process involving drastic harrowing of the sward to pull out old vegetation, followed by liming and fertilizers, particularly phosphate, to encourage the better grasses and clovers. If necessary, a seeds mixture could be broadcast on the field.

The use of stock to bite down the new growth and encourage tillering will bring about a gradual improvement of the sward. But it is only gradual, usually taking a number of years to upgrade the pasture. Various chemicals are now available to help destroy the mat more quickly, and, if necessary, a sod seeder can be used to plant the seeds into the soil. A more rapid improvement of the sward will follow. Some chemicals will completely kill the old sward, and the field can be re-seeded to grass without any cultural operations (see page 262).

### Haymaking

Too much poor quality hay is made in this country. Apart from the wet weather, poor quality herbage and inefficient methods of making are mainly responsible. Although crops such as lucerne, sainfoin and cereal/pulse mixtures can be used for hay, the cheapest and generally the most satisfactory crop is the grass/clover mixture.

The N.I.A.B. leaflet Grass for Conservation discusses in detail the stage for cutting grass consistent with digestibility and yield. In theory optimum digestibility is suggested at 63D (page 209), but in practice with haymaking, the D value is likely to be nearer 60. In the majority of grass species this will be at the ear-emergence stage.

The critical period for hay occurs when the crop is partly dried in the field, and therefore there is a *golden rule for haymaking*. No more hay should be ready for picking up in one day than can be dealt with by the equipment and staff. If the cutting outstrips the drying and collection, the hazards of weather damage are greatly increased. Thus, if the baler can only deal with, say, 8 hectares (20 acres) in the day, then cutting should be in 8 hectare lots.

The object in haymaking should be to dry the crop as rapidly as possible without too much exposure to sun and the least possible movement after the crop is partially dry. Consequently, there are only two methods of making hay worth considering:

(a) The quick haymaking method whereby the crop is baled in the quickest possible time consistent with its safety.
(b) Barn drying of hay.

QUICK HAYMAKING

With this method, there can be two or three stages in the making of hay.

(1)(i)   Fresh Crop            75–80% moisture content
                                       Curing in the field.
(ii)         approximately 25%     m.c.
                                       Drying in the bale in the field.
(2)(iii)    approximately 20–23% m.c.
                                       Drying in the stack.
           Hay—safe for storage 18% m.c.

(1)(i) *Curing in the field.* The crop should be cut when it is dry and when the weather appears to be set fine. The local meteorological office will give a weather forecast for 2–3 days ahead. If possible the headlands of the field should be cut earlier for silage. Hay on the headland usually takes longer to dry out than the rest of the field. So that the crop should be cut quickly when the forecast is right, high speed uninterrupted mowing is imperative. The ordinary reciprocating knife mower will not give the best performance with heavy laid crops, and although double-knife mowers will achieve fast cutting under almost any conditions, maintenance is more difficult. Horizontal rotary mowers with a 1·5 m (5 ft) working width have a high performance under all conditions, and although there is little curing effect, the swath is left in good condition for subsequent treatment. The flail mower has been developed from the forage harvester, but bruising is less severe, and the material is left in a satisfactory state for rapid drying. With both the rotary and flail mower ample power must be available to ensure maximum cutting rate. Of course the flail harvester, with modifications, can be used most successfully for cutting, but generally conditioning treatment is rather severe, and although it will set the pattern for very quick drying, there can be heavy loss of dry matter in the field, even with subsequent gentle treatment.

As soon as the crop has been cut it should be moved. The tedder is ideal to use following a flail (not forage harvester) or rotary mower. Better results may be obtained by alternating the turner (to invert the swath on to dry ground) with the tedder. As soon as the top is drier than the bottom of the broken swath, it should be turned, and this may have to be repeated again on the first day. (If the crop was cut with the reciprocating mower the use of the crimper, or crusher (more suitable for legumes), or flail hay-maker within 20 minutes of cutting will certainly quicken the rate of drying. Thereafter, on the first day, the crop should be treated with the tedder and turner as above.) The next morning, when the dew is off the ground, it should again be moved as on the previous day, but as it gets drier (and/or depending on the amount of leaf present) more gentle handling is necessary, using only the turner. On the third day, when the dew is gone, the crop should be turned, perhaps twice, and then it may possibly be ready for baling. But this does depend on the weather, the size and type of crop, and it may be *at least* another day before the hay is fit to bale.

Only general principles using basic implements have been discussed for field curing. The importance of preserving the leaf cannot be over-emphasized. In the past there has perhaps been a tendency to stress the green colour of the hay as the only index of well-cured hay. Sometimes this has been achieved at the expense of the leaf.

Although it is convenient to talk in terms of moisture content in connection with stages of drying, there is at present no reliable moisture meter to test the moisture content of the crop in the field. It is a question of experience in deciding when the hay is fit to bale. As a guide, Table 17 devised by Mr. Gordon Shepperson of The National Institute of Agricultural Engineering, shows the condition of the hay crop at varying stages of moisture content.

TABLE 17. ASSESSMENT OF MOISTURE CONTENT OF HAY

| Moisture content % | Condition |
| --- | --- |
| 50–60 | Little surface moisture—leaves flaccid, juices easily extruded from stems or from leaves if pressed hard. |
| 40–50 | No surface moisture—parts of leaves becoming brittle. Juice easily extracted from stems if twisted in a small bundle. |
| 30–40 | Leaves begin to rustle and do not give up moisture unless rubbed hard. Moisture easily extruded from stems using thumb-nail or pen-knife, or with more difficulty by twisting in the hands. |
| 25–30 | Hay rustles—a bundle twisted in the hands will snap with difficulty, but should extrude no surface moisture. Thick stems extrude moisture if scraped with thumb-nail. |
| 20–25 | Hay rustles readily—a bundle will snap easily if twisted—leaves may shatter—a few juicy stems. |
| 15–20 | Swath-made hay fractures easily—snaps easily when twisted—juice difficult to extrude. |

(ii) *Drying in the bale.* Opinions differ as to whether the bales should be left in the field after baling to continue drying. If it is the intention to carry the bales immediately after baling it is probably wiser to bale with a lower moisture content (say about 23–25%) than when the bales are to be left for further drying. In this latter case it is preferable to make fair-sized heaps of bales and cover them with polythene, making sure that the polythene is kept clear of the bales to avoid condensation. Round bales are virtually weather proof and they may be left to dry slowly in the field for some weeks although obviously aftermath recovery of the grass will be very much retarded under the bales.

(2)(iii) *Drying in the stack.* There are various ways in which the bales can be picked up from the field prior to stacking.

The stack is usually built under a Dutch barn. With any type of stack a good level bottom is necessary, one formed of substantial rough timbers is ideal to keep the first layer of bales well clear of the ground.

The stack walls must be built carefully and firmly. Within the walls, the bales should be stacked leaving air spaces between them. They should not be squeezed in. There are two reasons for this:

(a) The moisture content at stacking will generally be about 22%. It will eventually drop to about 16%. This moisture must be allowed to escape.

(b) As the bales are not very dense, they will, in the lower layers of the stack, tend to be squeezed out by the weight of the bales above. Therefore, cavities between the bales will reduce the tendency of the walls to "belly out".

A good layer of straw should be put on top of the stack to soak up the escaping moisture. This will help to prevent the top layers of bales from going mouldy.

## THE BARN DRYING OF HAY

This is a process whereby partially dried herbage is dried sufficiently for storage by blowing air through it. When making hay in the field, it is in the final stages of curing—the reduction of moisture from about 35% to 25%—that demands all the skill and attention of the farmer. It is at this critical period that the major losses of dry matter take place through too severe handling, and damage by the weather. If the hay can be carried at an earlier stage for curing to be completed in the barn, or stack, it should be much leafier and more nutritious.

At present there is one basic method of barn drying.

*Storage-drying.* (a) With this system of drying, the bales (at 35–45% moisture content) are placed on a flat evenly ventilated flow through which air is forced by a fan. Drying takes place in a building with air-tight sides to encourage the air to flow through the bales.

(b) The Dutch system of barn hay drying, known as the *Radial-*

*Drying (Dutch) System*, can be used in existing open-sided barns without any false floor. Thus capital costs are reduced compared with storage drying as described above.

Bales are stacked, up to a total height of 20 layers, round a central "bung", and as stacking proceeds the bung is raised, leaving a

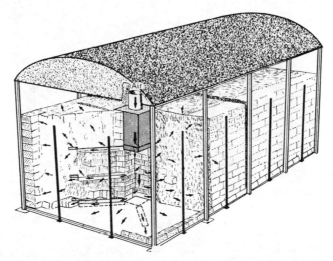

FIG. 67. Drying in the barn (Dutch system).

central, vertical chimney through which air is blown either from the top or from an underground air-duct. The air then flows radially outwards through the bales commencing after the first day's loading. Branch ducts in the diagonals of the stack ensure a more even flow of air to all the bales.

(c) The hay can also be dried in bays in an open-sided barn. Drying commences, from air blown through lateral ducts, when the bales are two layers above the duct up to a total height of about 17 bales (Figure 68).

There are various modifications of these barn-drying systems.

Whatever method is employed for drying, the importance of even wilting in the field cannot be over-emphasized. This is to ensure that subsequent drying of the bales will be as uniform as possible. Under normal conditions, 1–1½ days' curing in the field prior to baling will be necessary for the hay to be reduced to a moisture content of between 35–45%.

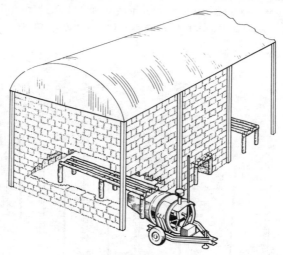

FIG. 68. A form of storage drying.

*New developments.* The "big-baler"—a machine producing bales weighing approximately 560 kg (11 cwt)—is now being used under farm conditions. Properly mechanised, the system does mean easier harvesting from field to barn, but handling for subsequent feeding may be difficult.

*Hay preservatives* have also recently been developed. They are a possible compromise between quick haymaking and barn-drying.

A chemical (which acts as a mould inhibitor) based on propionic acid is sprayed into the baling chamber to allow the hay to be baled at a somewhat higher moisture content (about 30%). This should reduce the loss of leaf in the field.

### TRIPODING OF HAY

Although good quality hay can be made by curing the crop on wooden frameworks in the field, it is a very slow and laborious method.

## Silage

Silage is produced by conserving green crops in a succulent state. The actual conservation process is known as ensilage and the container in which the material is placed is a silo. Good silage is a most valuable feeding stuff for both cattle and sheep.

CROPS FOR SILAGE

Grass is the most satisfactory crop for silage, and if it is cut at about the pre-flowering stage (but see N.I.A.B. leaflet, Grass for Conservation), it should provide a reasonable D value with a relatively high yield. Lacerated or chopped grass ensiles more easily than long material.

Many other crops can be ensiled such as:

(a) *Lucerne*. Sometimes this crop produces rather poor silage. This could be due to the alkaline minerals contained in the plant which would tend to lessen the acidity of the fermentation, thus encouraging the wrong type of bacteria.

(b) *Arable crops* often referred to as "whole crops" (see page 244).

(c) By-product silages, e.g. that produced from sugar-beet tops and pea-haulms, can be of high quality provided the material is ensiled clean.

## Silos

The size of silo varies—about 1 m³ weighs 0·75 t of made silage (1 ft³ weighs 45–50 lb silage). This will vary according to the degree of compaction.

Many types of silos are seen on farms in this country, but generally the most satisfactory are:

(1) Walled clamp silo (as under Dutch barn—Fig. 73). Very often the walls are railway sleepers. There is less side waste than with the unwalled clamp, and it is seen to best advantage under a Dutch barn. This type of silo is ideally suited to self-feeding.

(2) The Dutch barn silo (Fig. 73). The Dutch barn acts as a cover under which the silage can be made either in a clamp, stack or walled silo. The silage is protected all the time, and it should therefore be much drier. These silos are, of course, expensive, but in

Fig. 69. Stack silo.

Fig. 70. Pit silo.

Fig. 71. Run-over clamp.

Fig. 72. Wedge clamp.

FIG. 73. Dutch barn silo.

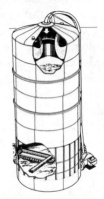

FIG. 74. Air-tight tower silo.

addition they can be used for storage of hay and straw, as well as possibly part of the building housing stock.

(3) Tower silo (Fig. 74). The modern tower silo is normally made of galvanized steel, and is glass-lined or treated with a protective paint to make it air-tight and acid resistant. A domed metal top completes the seal. Tower silos can also be made of wood, concrete or galvanized steel, but without any added protection to make them more air-tight.

Stack, clamp and pit silos without a cover are not commonly made these days. With the first two particularly there is a tendency for excessive wastage, and within reason the larger the silo the better, as this should mean a smaller proportion of wastage.

DRAINAGE OF SILOS

Unless the silo is well drained the bottom layers of silage will soon putrify. A simple drain is all that is necessary to get the effluent away. The simplest method is to have the silo floor sloping from one end to the other, with a cross drain at the lower end, although there are more expensive modifications.

## Harvesting the Crop for Silage

The *forage harvester* is the most commonly used machine for cutting and collecting the crop. But now the crop is often wilted in the field prior to being ensiled, and it could therefore be cut with the harvester, a flail cutter, a rotary or reciprocating mower. The forage harvester is used with high-sided trailers which collect the grass as it is blown from the "spout" of the harvester. Normally the trailer will dump its load by the silo which is then filled or built with the small buckrake.

The full-chop harvester which is considered necessary for high dry matter silage made in the tower is being used by some farmers for clamp silage. This will make the system more expensive, but apart from a better performance in the field, it should mean easier handling of the made silage if it is not to be self-fed.

## Silage Making (Ensilage)

THE FERMENTATION PROCESS

In silage making this is essentially a matter of the breakdown of the carbohydrate. It takes place in two stages:

(1) *By respiration and development of heat.* When the plant is cut off from its roots, and is placed in a silo. respiration is continued by the cells taking in oxygen from the air in the ensiled crop, and carbon dioxide from the carbohydrate is given off. This respiration and breakdown of the carbohydrate brings about a rise in temperature. The more air there is present the more the respiration and breakdown of carbohydrate.

(2) *By bacterial action.* Eventually, as the supply of free air lessens,

a different set of changes take place, whereby bacteria, which are always present on the green crop, act on the carbohydrate to produce organic acids. Two main acids can be produced by their respective bacteria, *lactic acid*, which is highly desirable, and *butyric acid* which is very undesirable.

Thus the stage is reached when the green crop is "pickled" in the acid; this, in fact, is silage, and what type of acid dominates depends upon the type of fermentation. This can be controlled to a large extent by the farmer himself.

As a result of different types of fermentation, three main types of silage can be produced as in Table 18.

COLD SILAGE

The development of heat brought about by respiration should, as far as is possible, be kept to a minimum. Provided the crop is wilted and dry, and/or additives are used to provide acid or sugar for the lactic bacteria, good silage can be made at temperatures of below 16°C (60°F) with little risk of butyric bacteria predominating. At this low temperature, there is less breakdown of carbohydrate compared with the old hot fermentation technique, and so a more valuable silage is produced.

*Additives.* The addition of *acid* additives such as formic acid or formalin and sulphuric acid will help ensure the acceptable acid conditions for the lactic acid bacteria. Acid additives are used at the rate of 2·25 litre/tonne ($\frac{1}{2}$ gal/ton) or an acid supplement such as calcium formate and sodium nitrate can be applied at 11–12 kg/tonne (5–6 lb/ton). It may be necessary to increase these levels if there are difficult conditions for the lactic bacteria.

*Molasses* (as a sugar additive) has been used for many years, but it is being superceded by acids. The recommended rate is 9–12 litre/tonne (2–3 gal/ton). But it is not easy to use, although it can be applied from a tank mounted on the forage-harvester, or diluted with warm water and sprayed onto the crop, either before or after cutting, by means of a low volume sprayer with large jets.

TABLE 18. TYPES OF SILAGE

| | Sample | Feeding value | Reasons | Prevention |
|---|---|---|---|---|
| Silage Overheated | Colour: brown to black. Smell: burnt sugar. Texture: dryish. | Although palatable, nutrionally is poor. Carbohydrates have been burnt up and protein digestibility considerably impaired by the high temperature. | Temperature remains at 49°C (120°F) or more, due to an appreciable amount of air present in the silo. This happens with stemmy and/or over-wilted material. | Do not let the crop get too mature before ensiling. When necessary fill the silo quickly and keep the air out. A stack silo should only be built in an emergency. |
| Butyric acid | Colour: drab, olive green. Smell: unpleasant and rancid. Texture: slimy, soft tissues easily rubbed from fibres. Taste: not sharp, pH 5·0 or over. | Reasonably palatable and nutritionally quite good, but this depends on the stage of butyric acid fermentation. With very butyric silage, palatability will be poor and much of the protein will have been broken down by the spoiling bacteria. In extreme cases the silage may become toxic, especially to younger stock. | The butyric acid bacteria are allowed to dominate, conditions being unfavourable for the growth of the desirable bacteria, i.e. when young, leafy and unwilted crops with a high moisture content are put into the silo, and also when soil contaminated crops (butyric acid bacteria most commonly occur in the soil) are ensiled. The growth of the lactic acid bacteria is slow under these conditions, and therefore they do not produce sufficient acid to prevent the butyric acid bacteria from maintaining and increasing their presence. | Create unfavourable conditions for the butyric acid bacteria, i.e. encourage the lactic acid bacteria. Ensile dry, and possibly wilted crops, and, if necessary (with a young sappy crop), use some form of additive. Create an intense acid medium as quickly as possible to keep out the butyric acid bacteria. |
| Lactic acid | Colour: bright light green to yellow-green. Smell: sharp and vinegary. Texture: firm soft tissue not easily rubbed from fibres. Taste: not sharp, pH 5·0 or over. Taste, sharply acid, pH 4·5 or less. | Good, and palatability should be excellent. | The lactic acid bacteria have dominated the ensiling process. They have grown rapidly to produce sufficient acid to keep out the spoiling bacteria. Dry conditions have favoured the lactic acid bacteria and if the ensiled crop has been young and leafy, an additive has been added to provide sugar or acid to stimulate the desirable bacteria. | Do not prevent, encourage! |

RULES FOR MAKING SILAGE

If a high dry matter silage is to be produced it is absolutely essential to ensile the crop in as dry a condition as possible. Unless it is very stemmy the crop should be wilted. Rate of wilting will depend on prevailing weather conditions and also the treatment the crop receives. The moisture content can be reduced by up to 10% (from an initial 75–80%) in the first 24 hours under *good* conditions where the crop receives no treatment after cutting. But if the crop is crimped or tedded immediately after cutting it can be reduced by at least 15% in 6 hours. Respiration and other losses occur with field wilting so this period should be reduced to a minimum.

SEALED SILAGE (Waltham or Dorset wedge system).

To produce silage with less waste it is essential to kill the respiring plant cell as quickly as possible. Thus air should be prevented from entering the green crop in the silo. The oxygen originally present is used up, and with no further air, the plant cell will die.

The walls of the silo should be made as air-tight as possible to prevent air getting into the ensiled crop. With a sleeper wall, a plastic sheet attached to the inside is quite satisfactory.

The silo is filled in the form of a wedge as in Fig. 75. The first trailer loads are tipped up against the end wall and subsequent loads are built up with a buckrake to form a wedge. At the end of the day the wedge is covered with plastic sheeting (500 gauge) attached to the end wall of the silo. The next day, after the sheet has been rolled back more crop is added to the wedge extending its length until the silo is filled. Care is taken to keep the completed part of the wedge covered all the time and the uncompleted section covered after each day's loading. After the silo has been filled, a thin covering of grass will help to keep the cover in position. To reduce side wastage particular attention must be paid to pressing the crop down at the sides. The tractor and buckrake will normally give sufficient consolidation although extra may be necessary at the start of each day's work. With this cold fermentation method, provided respiration is kept to a minimum, the temperature should not rise above 16°C (60°F).

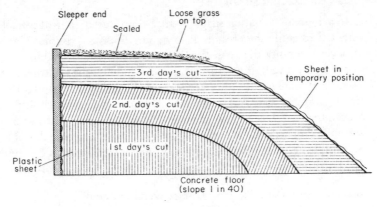

FIG. 75

The wedge-shape principle can also be used for a clamp silo without walls. In this case a plastic sheet is used to cover the wedge completely after each day's building, and at the completion of the silo.

### HIGH DRY MATTER SILAGE

High dry matter silage of between 35% and 50% dry matter is normally made in a tower as illustrated in Fig. 74, although on a large scale it is possible to make it in a sealed clamp.

Silage made in a tower follows the same principle as that of sealed clamp silage. In order to justify the high capital cost involved of tower, field and feeding equipment, the silage produced should have a high nutritive value capable of not only maintaining the animal, but also of making a significant contribution to its production ration. This means that prior to ensiling, the crop must be very well wilted, and loss of dry matter in the field can be as much as 15–20%, particularly when wet weather holds up field operations. This is one reason why "whole cereal" crops are now becoming popular again for towers. Cut in early July, crops such as barley and oats have a much higher dry matter content compared with grass, and no field wilting should be necessary. The digestibility and protein content of whole crop silage is not as high as grass silage.

Maize is also a useful crop for high dry matter silage (see page 142).

### Green Crop Drying

This is more commonly referred to as grass drying. It is the most efficient method of conservation because, compared with silage and haymaking, there is far less loss of digestible materials.

Apart from grass, crops such as whole crop cereals, maize, beans and forage rye will probably be used to an increasing extent in the future.

Two types of driers can be used:

(1) *The low temperature* (160°C (300°F)) *conveyor type.* Basically this consists of a horizontal cylinder through which the wet material is conveyed on a moving bed. Heated air is forced up through the bed to drive off the moisture. Output varies according to the initial moisture content of the crop (usually between 75% and 80%). With a crop previously field wilted (although carotene will be lost) it can be up to 0·7 tonne (14 cwt) of dried material per hour, although the average is nearer 300 kg. Two men are needed to operate the drier, but only one extra would be required with two conveyor driers run side by side. Until recently, this drier has been the main type used, but because of its low output it is being replaced by high temperature driers.

(2) *The high temperature* (up to 1100°C (approx. 2000°F)) *pneumatic rotary drum drier.* Drum driers are either single pass or triple pass, these terms describing the arrangement of the internal structure of the drum. The principle with this type of drier is that the wet crop, usually chopped into short lengths, is introduced into a stream of hot air. As the moisture is moved so the material gets lighter; it rises up and is blown away by another stream of air. An average output of about 3 tonne (3 tons) of dried material per hour can be expected when the crop is dried from 80% to 10% moisture content. But there are now much bigger capacity driers in operation with outputs as high as 10 tonnes per hour. For operation two men are

required, thus the labour charge per tonne of dried crop is considerably less than the conveyor drier. But these driers are extremely expensive with capital investments from £100,000 to £300,000.

Small on-farm machines are being developed and some of these are mobile units. Their maximum cost could be up to about £40,000.

At present grass makes up 75% and lucerne 25% of the tonnage dried in this country. To justify the high capital requirements for the operating plant and the high cost of producing dried grass it is essential that the crop should be cut at the correct stage of growth. If the dried crop is to be fed to ruminants rather than to poultry, the digestibility of the crop will assume a new significance. Hence it is important to see that as far as possible the crop is cut at its maximum digestibility. This should mean growing different species and varieties of species of herbage plants to give a sequence of maximum digestibility throughout the drying season from April to November. Plant breeders are now trying to produce varieties of herbage plants to give this ideal situation.

For the grass crop nitrogen usage up to 625 kg/ha (500 units/acre) per year (with the first 125 kg/ha (100 units/acre) going on in February) will normally be required. This in turn will necessitate potash application of up to 250 kg/ha (200 units/acre) depending on the soil type. Lucerne should not need any nitrogen but very often may require a total of 375 kg/ha (300 units/acre) of potash throughout the year.

Because of the high capital cost involved with green crop drying the future must lie with the development of the large unit normally on a co-operative basis. To run the drier efficiently, and to ensure that the right sort of crop is being dried, it is essential that the manager of a plant must have complete control not only of the drier but also the crops to be dried.

### Suggestions for Classwork

(1) Identify the grasses and clovers of agricultural importance, both in their vegetative and flowering stage.

(2) Examine a seeds mixture, and identify the different types of seeds.

(3) Compare the periods of production of a ryegrass and non-ryegrass sward.

(4) Study and compare different techniques of grazing dairy cows and beef cattle.

(5) Study and compare different methods of fattening lambs off grass.

(6) Visit a barn hay-drying plant, and compare barn dried hay with that made in the field.

(7) Examine different samples of silage, and make notes on the type of fermentation, dry matter content and amount of wastage present in the silo.

(8) Visit a grass-drying plant.

CHAPTER 6

# WEEDS

WEEDS are plants which are growing where they are not wanted.

## Harmful Effects of Weeds

(1) Weeds reduce yields by shading and smothering crops.

(2) Weeds compete with crops for plant nutrients and water.

(3) Weeds can spoil the quality of a crop and so lower its value, e.g. wild onion bulbils in wheat; ryegrass in a meadow fescue seed crop.

(4) Weeds can act as host plants for various pests and diseases of crop plants, e.g. charlock is a host for flea-beetles and club-root which attack brassica crops: fat hen and knotgrass are hosts for virus yellows and root eelworm of sugar-beet. Couch grasses are hosts for take-all and eyespot of cereals.

(5) Weeds such as bindweed, cleavers and thistles can hinder cereal harvesting and increase the cost of drying the grain.

(6) Weeds such as thistles, buttercups, docks, ragwort, etc., can reduce the grazing area and feeding value of pastures. Some grassland weeds may taint milk when eaten by cows, e.g. buttercups, wild onion.

(7) Weeds such as ragwort, horsetails, nightshade, foxgloves and hemlock are poisonous and if eaten by stock are likely to cause unthriftiness or death. Fortunately, stock normally do not eat poisonous weeds.

## Spread of Weeds

Weeds become established in various ways such as:

(1) *From seeds:*

(a) sown with crop seeds—this is most likely where a farmer uses his own seed and it is not properly cleaned.
(b) shed in previous years; some weed seeds can remain dormant in the soil for up to 60 years.
(c) carried onto the field by birds and animals, or by the wind.
(d) in farmyard manure, e.g. docks and fat hen.

(2) *Vegetatively from:*

(a) pieces of *rhizomes* (underground stems), e.g. couch (twitch); creeping thistle, field bindweed and coltsfoot.
These pieces are usually carried about on field implements.
(b) pieces of *stolons* (surface runners), e.g. watergrass (bent grass).
(c) pieces of *roots*, e.g. docks and ragwort.

### Control of Weeds

In recent years, the introduction of chemical *herbicides* or *weedicides* has greatly simplified the problem of controlling many weeds. Most of these chemicals can act in a *selective* manner by killing weeds growing in arable crops and grassland. The control of weeds with herbicides is now becoming an established and necessary practice on most farms. Nevertheless, it is worth remembering that other good husbandry methods can still play an important part in controlling weeds.

Methods used to control weeds are:

(1) *Cultivations* (see pp. 88, 89).
(2) *Cutting*, e.g. bracken, rushes, ragwort, thistles. This weakens the plants and prevents seeding. The results are often disappointing.
(3) *Drainage.* This is a very important method of controlling weeds which can thrive in waterlogged soils. Lowering the water-table by good drainage will help to control weeds such as rushes, sedges and creeping buttercup.
(4) *Rotations.* By growing leys and various arable crops there is an opportunity of tackling weeds in many ways and at various

times of the year. This method has become less important since herbicides were introduced.

(5) *Maintenance of good fertility.* Arable crops and good grass require a high level of fertility, i.e. the soil must be adequately supplied with lime, nitrogen, phosphates, potash and humus. Under these conditions crops can compete strongly with most weeds.

(6) *Chemical control.* It is outside the scope of this book to deal in detail with this very involved subject. However, the following is a summary of the main chemicals and methods which are used.

Most of the chemicals used have a *selective* effect, i.e. they are substances which stunt or kill weeds and have little or no harmful effects on the crop in which the weeds are growing. A severe check of weed growth is usually sufficient to prevent seeding and to allow the crop to grow away strongly.

Most of the common weeds found in cereals can now be controlled by selective herbicides. It is hoped, eventually, to have chemicals to control all weeds in all crops.

Herbicides are usually sold under a wide range of proprietary names which can be very confusing—especially if the common name of the active material is not stated. Throughout this book, the common name of the chemical is used when referring to herbicides and, occasionally, where there is only one proprietary product, the trade name is also given. A list of proprietary names of approved products is published annually in a free booklet which can be obtained from the M.A.F.F.

The *selectivity of a herbicide* depends on such factors as those summarized below:

(a) The *chemical* itself and its *formulation*, e.g. whether it is in water-soluble, emulsion or dust form; also whether wetters or spreaders have been added.

(b) The amount of the *active ingredient* applied and the quantity of carrier (water, oil or dust). Most herbicides are applied in water solution.

| Volume rates for spraying | | litres/ha | gals/acre |
|---|---|---|---|
| Very low volume | up to | 56 | 5 |
| Low volume | | 56– 220 | 5– 20 |
| Medium volume | | 220– 670 | 20– 60 |
| High volume | | 670–1120 | 60–100 |

(c) The *stage of growth* of the crop and the weeds. In general, weeds are easier to kill in the young stages of growth. However, treatment may have to be delayed until the crop is far enough advanced to be resistant to damage.

(d) *Weather* conditions. The action of some chemicals is reduced by cold air temperatures and rain after spraying.

The chemicals now commonly used as herbicides can be grouped as follows:

(1) *Contact herbicides.* These will kill most plant tissues with which they come in contact but they do not move through the plant. Shoots of perennial plants may be killed but regrowth from the underground parts usually occurs. Some examples of contact herbicides are *diquat, dinoseb, mineral oils, pentachlorphenol (PCP), sulphuric acid, ioxynil* and *bromoxynil.*

(2) *Residual herbicides.* When applied to the soil these chemicals persist for some time and kill weeds as they germinate. Some of these are selective, e.g. *simzaine, atrazine, propham (IPC), endothal, linuron, prometryne* and *pyrazon.*

(3) *Total herbicides.* These chemicals are used to kill all plant growth, e.g. on paths and other such areas. They are most effective on germinating seedlings, e.g. *simazine, atrazine, monuron, borax* and *sodium chlorate.*

(4) *Translocated herbicides.* This type of chemical moves about within the plant after being absorbed through the leaves or roots, e.g. the "hormone" or "growth regulators"; also *dalapon, amino-triazole* and *barban.*

(5) *The hormone (growth regulator) herbicides.* These are a special group of translocated chemicals which are similar to substances produced naturally by plants and which can regulate and control the growth of some plants. They are mostly used for controlling weeds in cereals and some can be used on grassland. The important ones are: MCPA, 2,4-D, mecoprop, dichlorprop, MCPB, 2,4-DB, MCPA/2,3,6-TBA and MCPA/dicamba.

## Weed Control in Cereals

Cereals used to be regarded as the dirty crops in the rotation until the introduction of MCPA in 1942. This, and the very similar 2,4-D, easily killed all the troublesome and aggressive broad-leaved weeds at that time—especially yellow charlock, poppy and fat hen, but it was necessary to use these chemicals for many years to destroy seedlings developing each year from the large numbers of dormant seeds in the soil. After a time these weeds more or less disappeared from many fields, but others, which were resistant to MCPA, were able to grow and set seed without competition from the more aggressive weeds such as yellow charlock. Weeds such as chickweed and cleavers then became troublesome and in 1956 two herbicides—CMPP (now known as mecoprop) and TBA/MCPA mixture were introduced and these proved effective against the chickweed and cleavers as well as the weeds which were controlled by MCPA. Later, another resistant group has developed—the polygonums (redshank, black bindweed and knotgrass) and to deal with these 2,4-DP (now known as dichlorprop) and dicamba/MCPA mixture were introduced in 1961; knotgrass is still proving a difficult one to deal with. Now, another group is developing—the mayweeds—and a new range of chemicals such as mixtures including ioxynil or bromoxynil are being used.

In all these cases the chemicals used usually justify their use for several reasons such as:

higher crop yields when weed competition is removed;

easier harvesting because there is little or no green weed material in the crop to delay drying in showery weather, also, seed heads of weeds such as poppies, mayweeds and thistles are not allowed to develop and cause drying and cleaning problems.

However, although MCPA is a cheap chemical, some of the newer herbicides (called "broad-spectrum" herbicides), which kill most of the weeds occurring now-a-days, are much more expensive and in some cases the benefits may not justify the cost. Also, greater care is sometimes required when applying them if crop damage is to be avoided.

It is not possible to use herbicides such as MCPA, mecropop, dichlorprop, TBA and dicamba mixtures, ioxynil and bromoxynil mixtures on cereal crops undersown with clovers or other legumes. However, it was discovered that the butyric chemicals MCPB or 2,4-DB did not damage clovers but killed many of the weeds controlled by MCPA with the exception of yellow charlock, runch and hempnettle. The addition of benazolin gives a wide spectrum kill of the most troublesome weeds in undersown crops—especially chickweed. Dinoseb may also be required (see page 256).

Perennial broad-leaved weeds are not so easily killed as the annuals—especially thistles, field bindweed, wild onion and docks—because the foliage usually develops after the normal spraying time for the annuals. Field bindweed is often very troublesome—causing lodging and great difficulty in combining because of the mass of green growth. However, it can be effectively killed by spraying with MCPA or 2,4-D about 2–3 weeks before harvest. The damage, if any, caused by the sprayer wheel marks is negligible in a lodged crop. Stubble treatment is occasionally effective.

Annual weeds are much easier to kill as seedlings. However, the safest time for spraying cereals is between the five-leaf and jointing stages of growth (see Fig. 76) when some weed seedlings are becoming well established. There are exceptions to this, e.g. oats can be sprayed with MCPA after the first leaf stage; also, mecoprop, dichlorprop, and ioxynil, bromoxynil and bentazon mixtures can be used at the 3–4 leaf stage.

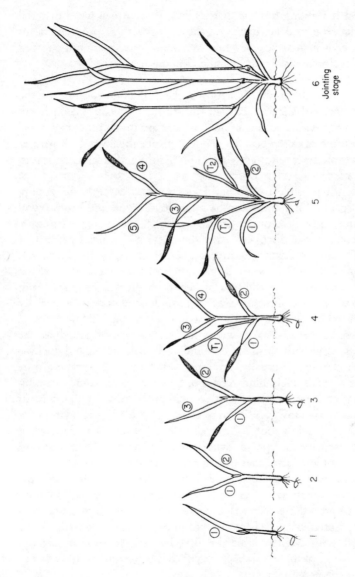

Fig. 76. Diagram to show the leaf stages in the cereal plant. $T_1$ and $T_2$ are tillers.

The following common weeds are easily and cheaply controlled by MCPA (or 2,4-D):

| | | |
|---|---|---|
| annual nettle | hempnettle (not 2,4-D) | poppy |
| buttercups | mustards | rush (common, soft) |
| charlock | orache | shepherd's purse |
| docks (seedlings) | pennycress | thistles |
| fat hen | plantains | wild radish (runch) |

Table 19 summarizes the cheapest recommended herbicides (but not the only ones) which could be used on weeds not controlled by MCPA or 2,4-D. For crops undersown with clover, a small amount of MCPA may be included in the spray to deal with weeds not controlled by MCPB or 2,4-DB, for example charlock.

It is sometimes possible to control a wider spectrum of weeds, than those given above, with MCPA if it is applied at an earlier stage of growth of the weeds and cereals; to avoid damaging the cereals, a lower than normal dose of MCPA must be used. This practice can reduce spraying costs in some seasons, but it cannot be relied on every season, so it may be necessary to apply a second spray using the proper chemical for the troublesome weeds. Some farmers make up their own "cocktails" with various chemicals and the results are often quite satisfactory and cheap; however, this is a risky practice and it should only be done after seeking expert advice.

The *Wild Oat* is now a very serious weed problem on many farms, and whatever control measures are used it is likely to persist for a long time because of dormant seeds in the soil. This dormancy problem is made worse if stubble cultivations are carried out after harvest, because most of the shed seeds, if left on the soil surface, are destroyed or disappear in various ways. Hand roguing should be done when wild oats first appear in a field, but later, as the numbers increase, herbicides will have to be used in wheat and barley crops to avoid serious yield losses. The main herbicides which are giving good results are:

*Tri-allate* ("Avadex")—this is sprayed on the soil and lightly worked in before planting wheat or barley in autumn or spring; it can also be applied as tiny granules after planting: surviving wild oats usually grow normally.

TABLE 19

| MCPA controlled weeds plus | Straight cereals | Undersown with clover |
|---|---|---|
| Chickweed, cleavers, fumitory | Mecoprop | Benazolin plus MCPA, MCPB or 2,4-DB |
| Black bindweed, redshank, spurrey | Dichlorprop, dicamba mixture | 2,4-DB (not spurrey) |
| Mayweed, knotgrass | Mixtures containing ioxynil, bromoxynil or dicamba | Dinoseb |
| Shepherd's needle | Dinoseb | Dinoseb |
| Corn marigold | Dinoseb, ioxynil or bromoxynil mixtures, bentazon | Dinoseb |
| Speedwell | Ioxynil mixture | Dinoseb |

**Note.** Dinoseb is very poisonous; protective clothing must be worn. For fuller details on weed control in cereals see M.A.F.F. leaflet STL. 19.

*Barban* ("Carbyne" or "Oatex")—this can be applied to all wheat and most barley varieties when the wild oats are at the 1-to-2½-leaf stage; surviving wild oats are severely stunted.

*Benzoylprop ethyl* ("Suffix")—this can be applied to winter and spring wheat crops after they have tillered; some dwarfed wild oats usually survive.

*Chlorfenprop methyl* ("Bidisin")—can be applied to spring wheat and spring barley (including undersown crops) when the wild oats is at the 2-to-4-leaf stage. (Some varieties of oats are tolerant.)

Some other herbicides, for example "Dicurane", which are used mainly to control blackgrass will also give some control of wild oats. Tri-allate and barban give some control of blackgrass. (See also M.A.F.F. advisory leaflet No. 452, Wild Oats.)

*Blackgrass* is a very serious problem on many farms where the soils are of a heavy type and wet in winter, and where autumn sown crops are often grown. Most of the seeds of this weed germinate in the autumn, but enough can germinate in the spring in badly infested fields to seriously reduce yields. The following herbicides are recommended for control of blackgrass, as well as some broad-leaved weeds, in winter wheat and barley:

*Chlortoluron* ("Dicurane")—pre-emergence and post-emergence of the cereal. (Some varieties of wheat may be damaged.)

*Metoxuron* ("Dosanex")—post-emergence (as for "Dicurane").

*Metoxuron plus simazine* ("Fylene")—post-emergence.

*Methabenzthiazuron* ("Tribunil")—pre-emergence, wheat only.

*Terbutryne* ("Prebane 50")—pre-emergence.

(See also M.A.F.F. leaflet STL No. 92, Blackgrass.)

*Couch* (*twitch*) can be controlled fairly well between cereal crops by spraying the leaves in early autumn with *dalapon* and/or *amino-triazole* (the latter may also destroy docks and creeping thistle). TCA, sprayed on and worked into the soil, gives very good couch control. Repeated sprayings—every 2 to 3 weeks in autumn—with small doses of *paraquat* ("Gramoxone") considerably weakens and may kill couch; this is an exhausting technique and an application of nitrogen will encourage the shoots to develop quickly between sprayings in low fertility conditions.

*Creeping* or *arable bent* (*watergrass*) can be destroyed by a single large dose of *paraquat*.

A new herbicide—*glyphosate* ("Round-Up")—has given very good control of couch and many other problem weeds in the autumn.

## Chemical Weed Control in Potatoes, Roots and Kale

*Potatoes*

Following limited, or no cultivations after planting, the field is sprayed with one or more chemicals when the first potato shoots appear. Various contact and residual chemicals can be used; *dinoseb linuron, monolinuron, terbutryne* and *trietazine* are the main chemicals used either alone or with *paraquat* when wild oats and grass weeds are present. They act both as contact and residual herbicides and control most of the troublesome annual weeds. *Metabromuron* acts as a residual herbicide. Perennial weeds such as creeping (field) thistle, and bindweed are not controlled in this way but spraying the crop later with MCPA can control them although this treatment may reduce the yield of some varieties. Couch may be tackled in the autumn before planting as indicated under cereals (see p. 257) or by working EPTC into the soil during the three-week period before planting.

*Sugar-beet* and *Mangolds*

Most of the troublesome annual weeds in sugar beet are now controlled by pre-emergence herbicides; these are sprayed on the surface or lightly worked into the soil in 150 mm (6 in.) wide bands along the rows of beet, or, overall, where inter-row hoeing will not be done. The dose rate and efficiency of these herbicides is determined by soil type (and weather), and expert advice should be followed. The main herbicides recommended are:

  *endothal* + *propham* + *medinoterb*—("Murbetex Plus");
  *lenacil*—("Venzar"); *pyrazon*—("Pyramin");
  *propham* + *chlorpropham* + *fenuron*—("Beet-Kleen", "Herbon Gold", "Premalox", "Pyrafen", and "Quintex").

Wild oats can be usefully suppressed by several chemicals such as TCA, *propham* and *di-allate* ("Avadex") worked into the seedbed before sowing, or by post-emergence treatment with *barban* or *dalapon*.

Contact chemicals such as *diquat*, *dimexan* and *pentachlorphenol* can sometimes be used to kill faster-growing weeds which have emerged before the beet. Other contact herbicides such as phenmedipham ("Betanal E") may be used post-emergence to control weeds which escaped control by the pre-emergent herbicide.

Couch grasses should be controlled in the autumn before sowing as suggested under Cereals (page 257).

Very good chemical weed control is necessary if the "drilling-to-a-stand" technique is to be successful.

*Kale, Swede, and Turnip*

Couch should be controlled in the previous autumn or by early spring treatment with TCA.

Wild oats are suppressed by working into the soil di-allate ("Avedex") at drilling time or TCA about 7 days earlier.

Many annual broad-leaved weeds can be controlled by triflurin ("Treflan") worked into the soil during the fortnight before drilling or spraying propachlor ("Ramrod") on the soil before crop emergence.

Annual weeds are unlikely to be troublesome where these crops are slit-seeded into a chemically destroyed grass sward.

It is possible to control annuals by allowing them to germinate and then destroying them with a contact herbicide such as *diquat* or *diamexan* before drilling the crop.

In kale crops, many troublesome annual weeds, especially fat hen, can be controlled by post-emergence spraying with *desmetryne* ("Semeron"). Gas liquor and sulphuric acid have also been used, with reasonable effect, to control weeds such as charlock in the growing crop.

(See also M.A.F.F. leaflet STL 29, Weed control in root crops and kale.)

### Weed Control in Grassland

In arable crops, most damage is caused by annual weeds, but in established grassland biennial and perennial weeds cause most trouble. The presence of the weeds causes a *reduction in yield, nutrient quality* and *palatability* of the sward. Stock do not like grazing near buttercups, thistles and wild onions. Some weeds are *poisonous*, e.g. ragwort and horsetails, and some can *taint milk* if eaten, e.g. buttercups and wild onion.

Weeds in grassland are encouraged by such factors as:

(a) *Bad drainage*, e.g. rushes, sedges, horsetails and creeping buttercup.

(b) *Shortage of lime*, e.g. poor grasses (bents), sorrels.

(c) *Low fertility:* many weeds can live in conditions which are too poor for good types of grasses and clovers.

(d) *Poaching* (trampling in wet weather): the useful species are killed and weeds grow on the bare spaces.

(e) *Over-grazing:* this exhausts the productive species and allows poor, unpalatable plants such as bent, Yorkshire fog, thistles and ragwort to become established.

(f) *Continuous cutting* for hay encourages weeds such as soft brome, yellow rattle, knapweed and meadow barley grass.

Chemicals are a useful aid to controlling grassland weeds but should not be regarded as an alternative to good management.

The main chemicals used are MCPB and 2,4-DB—these do not harm the clovers. If clovers are abundant, and if resistant weeds such as ragwort are present, then MCPA or 2,4-D may be used as a much cheaper and more effective remedy.

Table 19 is a guide to the control of the more troublesome weeds.

WEED CONTROL WHEN RE-SEEDING

When re-seeding a grass sward, without a cover crop, weeds can be troublesome—especially annuals such as charlock, chickweed and

TABLE 20

| Weed | Control |
|---|---|
| Bracken | Cut or crush the fronds (leaves) twice a year when they are almost fully opened. If possible, plough deep and crop with potatoes, rape or kale before re-seeding. Rotavating about 250 mm. deep chops up and destroys the rhizomes. Very good chemical control is now possible with *dicamba* (spring) and *asulam* (mid-summer). |
| Buttercups | Spray with MCPA or MCPB. The bulbous buttercup is the most resistant type. |
| Daisies | Spray with 2,4-D or MCPA. |
| Docks | Seedlings and curled-leaved type—spray with MCPA or MCPB. Broad-leaved type—plough and take cleaning crop, e.g. kale. Grazing with sheep is helpful. Asulam gives good control when sprayed on the expanded leaves in the spring or autumn. |
| Horsetail | If possible, improve drainage. Spraying with MCPA or 2,4-D will kill aerial parts only and regrowth occurs—but if it is done 2–3 weeks before cutting, the hay crop should be safe for feeding. |
| Nettles | Spray with 2,4,5-T alone or in mixtures. |
| Ragwort | Cut before buds develop, to prevent seeding. Spray with 2,4-D or MCPA before the flower buds appear. Grazing with sheep in winter is helpful. |
| Rushes | Improve drainage, if possible. Common or soft rush—spray with MCPA or 2,4-D. Hard and jointed rushes—cut several times per year. Encourage grasses and clovers by good management. |
| Sorrel | Spray with MCPA or 2,4-D. Apply lime. |
| Thistles | Spray with MCPA or MCPB. The more resistant creeping type should be sprayed in the early flower-bud stage. Avoid over-grazing. |
| Tussock grass | Improve drainage. Cut off the "tussocks" with flail harvester or topper. |

fat hen. These can be controlled by topping in the young stages with the mower or by spraying with herbicides—this is especially desirable when chickweed is present.

Where grassland has to be re-seeded and ploughing is not possible, or undesirable, the old sward can be destroyed by spraying with *paraquat, dalapon, glyphosate* (new), or amino-triazole. An earlier application of 2,4-D may be worthwhile to destroy broad-leaved perennial weeds.

### Spraying with Herbicides

This is a skilled operation and should be carefully carried out. Some of the more important precautions to take are:

(1) Make a careful survey of the field to determine the weeds to be controlled; choose the most suitable chemical and best time for spraying.

(2) Check carefully the amount of chemical to be applied per acre and the volume of water to be used (220–330 l/ha is a common range). Make sure the chemical is thoroughly mixed with the water before starting. Soluble and wettable powders should be mixed with some water before adding to the tank. Use the agitator if necessary.

The rate of application is mainly controlled by the forward speed of the tractor (use a speedometer), and the size of nozzle, and to a lesser extent by the pressure (follow the maker's instructions). Always use clean, preferably not hard, water. Always use a filter. An accurate dipstick is necessary when re-filling the tank if it is not emptied each time.

(3) When using poisonous chemicals, e.g. dinoseb, it is necessary to wear fully protective clothing (read carefully the instructions issued with such chemicals). Do not blow out blocked nozzles.

(4) Do not spray on a windy day—especially with the hormone type of herbicides and if the spray is likely to blow onto susceptible crops or gardens. Keeping the boom as low as possible and using a plastic spray guard can be helpful; also using higher volume (larger droplets) is better than a very low volume mist for avoiding spray drift.

(5) Special types of sprayers using vibrating booms or vibrating nozzles reduce the risk of drift to a minimum.

(6) Make sure that the boom is level and that the spray cones or fans meet just above the level of the weeds to be controlled.

(7) Spray the headlands first; when spraying the rest of the field the drill rows in cereal crops are a useful guide. If using a wide boom it is advisable to use markers; avoid "misses" by slight over-lapping.

(8) Wash out sprayer thoroughly on waste ground and leave full of clean water—this avoids scale forming inside the tank which is one of the commonest causes of blockages in the nozzles.

(9) Do not mix different herbicides and insecticides in the sprayer without seeking advice on the matter; only some can be mixed.

As an alternative to *overall* spraying, *band* spraying, is often used when applying herbicides to root crops, e.g. sugar-beet. A band about 6 in. wide is sprayed over each row of seeds; the weeds between the rows are controlled by cultivations. This is especially useful when expensive chemicals are being used.

### Suggestions for Classwork

1. Examine seedlings of the common agricultural weeds in your area and learn how to identify them. Helpful pictures of weeds are published by the leading firms marketing herbicides.
2. When visiting farms make notes on the sprays used to control weeds, e.g. the main weeds, the chemicals used, time and methods of application.

CHAPTER 7

# PESTS AND
# DISEASES OF FARM CROPS

PESTS are responsible for millions of pounds of damage to agricultural crops in this country every year. Before discussing the various methods used to control pests, it is important to understand something of their structure and general habits.

One of the major groups of pests are the *insects*. They are *invertebrates*, i.e. they belong to a group of animals which do not possess an internal skeleton. Their bodies are supported by a hard external covering—the *exoskeleton*. It is composed chiefly of *chitin*, and is segmented so that the insect is able to move.

From the diagram of the external structure of an insect (see Fig. 77) it can be seen that the segments are grouped into three main parts:

1. *The head*, on which is found:

   (a) The *antannae*—or feelers carrying sense organs—e.g. smelling.

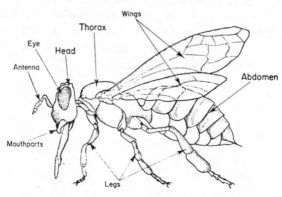

FIG. 77. Structure of an insect.

264

(b) The *eyes*—a number of single and a pair of compound eyes are present in most species.

(c) The *mouthparts*—(see Fig. 78). Two main types are found in insects:

    (i) the biting type.

    (ii) the sucking type—insects in this group suck the sap from the plant and do not eat the foliage.

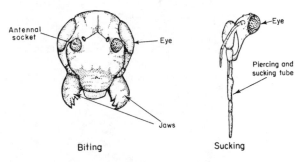

Biting          Sucking

FIG. 78. Insect mouthparts.

The type of mouthpart possessed by the insect is of considerable importance in deciding on the method of control.

2. *The thorax*, which bears:

    (a) The *legs*—there are always three pairs of jointed legs on adult insects.

    (b) The *wings*—found on most, but not on all, species.

3. The *abdomen*, which has no structures attached to it except in certain female species where the egg laying apparatus may protrude from the end.

### Life-cycles

A knowledge of the life-cycles of insects can be of great help in deciding on the best stage at which the insects will be most susceptible to control methods.

Most insects begin life as a result of an egg having been laid by the female. What emerges from the egg, according to the species, may or may not look like the adult insect.

There are two main types of life-cycles:

(1) The "complete" or four-stage life-cycle (see Fig. 79).

 (a) The *egg*.

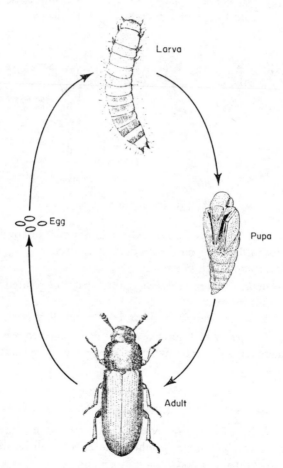

FIG. 79. Four-stage life-cycle.

(b) The *larva* (plural larvæ)—entirely different in appearance from the adult. This is the active eating and growing stage. The larvæ usually possess biting mouthparts, and it is at this stage with many insects that they are most destructive to crops on which they feed.

(c) The *pupa*—the resting stage. The larvæ pupate and undergo a complete change from which emerges—

(d) The *adult* insect—this feeds on crops but in many cases does far less damage than the larvæ.

(2) The "incomplete" or three-stage life-cycle (see Fig. 80).

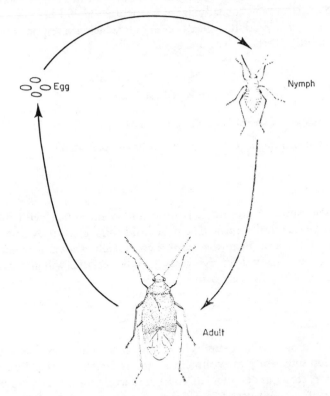

Fɪɢ. 80. Three-stage life-cycle.

(a) The *egg*.
(b) The *nymph*—this is very similar in appearance to the adult, although it is smaller and may not possess wings. It is the active eating and growing stage.
(c) The *adult* insect.

Most insects and/or larvæ and nymphs feeding on crops depend on these crops for part or all of their existence. The crop is the *host* plant, whilst the insect is the *parasite* to the host. Not all insects are parasitic; some are known as *predatory* insects in that they prey on other insects, killing and eating them. Some of these are beneficial to the farmer, e.g. the ladybird is particularly useful because, both as the larva and adult, it feeds on aphids which are responsible for transmitting certain virus diseases in plants.

### Methods of Pest Control

1. INDIRECT CONTROL MEASURES

These aim more at the prevention of the pest attack.

### (a) *Rotations*

As a means of control it is now not so important with more effective chemical control. The principal behind control by rotation is that if the host plant (the crop) is continually grown in the same field for too many successive years, then the parasite will increase in large numbers, e.g. eelworm.

### (b) *Time of sowing*

(i) A crop may sometimes be sown early enough so that it can develop sufficiently to withstand an insect attack, e.g. frit fly.
(ii) A crop can be sown late enough to avoid the peak emergence of a pest, e.g. flea-beetle.

### (c) Cultivations

Ploughing exposes pests such as wireworms, leatherjackets and caterpillars, which are then eaten by birds. Well prepared seed-beds encourage rapid germination and growth. This will often enable a crop to grow away from pest attack.

### (d) Encouragement of growth

Good quality seed should be used which will germinate quickly and evenly. It is also important that the crop is not checked to any extent, say by lack of a plant food. A poor growing crop is far more vulnerable to pest attack than a quick growing crop. A top-dressing of nitrogen, just as a crop is being attacked, may sometimes save the crop.

### (e) Clean farming

Weeds are alternate hosts to a great variety of insects, and, as far as possible, these sources of infestation should be eradicated.

## 2. BIOLOGICAL CONTROL

A parasite or predator is used to control the pest. The method has little application in farming in this country. In horticulture, the red spider mite is successfully controlled in cucumber production under glass by predator mites.

## 3. DIRECT CONTROL MEASURES

This means chiefly chemical control using a pesticide. These can be used in a number of ways, e.g.

Sprays and dusts.
A granular form for controlling aphids.
Baits for controlling soil pests such as leatherjackets, slugs and snails.
Seed dressing—mainly for the protection of cereals against wireworm, and brassica crops against flea-beetle. Usually the

insecticides are combined with a fungicide such as an organo-mercury compound.

Gases, smokes, fumigants are commonly used in greenhouses against aphids chiefly, and in granaries against beetles and weevils.

Basically, there are two ways in which pesticides kill pests:

## (1) *By contact*

The pest is killed when it comes in contact with the chemical, either when:

(a) it is directly hit by the spray or dust,
(b) it picks up the pesticide as it moves over foliage which has been treated,
(c) it absorbs vapour,
(d) it passes through soil which has also been treated.

## (2) *By ingestion*

As a *stomach* poison the pest eats the foliage treated with the pesticide, or the chemical is used in a bait.

As a *systemic* compound it is applied to the foliage or to the soil around the base of the plant. It gets into the sap stream of the plant and thus the pest is poisoned when it subsequently sucks the sap.

Most pesticides kill by more than one method, which makes them very effective. But many of them are extremely toxic to animals and humans, and by law, certain precautions must be observed by the persons using them.

## Classification of Pesticides

INSECTICIDES

(a) *The chlorinated hydrocarbons*

These insecticides are all stomach and contact poisons and the main ones are:

(a) *BHC.* As a spray and dust it is used extensively on fruit crops and it controls, amongst other insects, aphids, caterpillars and weevils. It is also a useful soil insecticide for control of wireworm and leatherjackets, but it can taint some crops such as potatoes.

(b) *DDT.* This is generally the most useful insecticide. It controls a wide range of both agricultural and fruit crop pests. Most beetles, caterpillars and weevils are susceptible to DDT. It can be used as a spray and a dust.

(c) *Aldrin.* This is best used as a soil insecticide. It controls wireworms and leatherjackets without any risk of taint in subsequent crops.

(d) *Dieldrin.* This is a particularly useful insecticide for controlling cabbage root fly as a dip.

It is now recommended that aldrin, dieldrin and DDT be restricted in their application because they are so persistent, and it is feared that their continued use may contaminate our environment.

Aldrin may still be used against wireworm in potatoes, but it must be applied separately and not compounded in fertilizers.

Restrictions on the use of DDT are likely in the near future.

## (b) *The organo-phosphorus compounds*

As a group, these insecticides are far more dangerous to use and they should be handled strictly in accordance with the manufacturer's instructions. An asterisk marks those chemicals included in the Agriculture (Poisonous Substances) Regulations. Certain precautions (including the use of protective clothing) must by law be taken when using these chemicals and it is advisable to read the official leaflet "The Safe Use of Poisonous Chemicals on the Farm" (ASP/1).

The following are examples of some of the organo-phosphorus insecticides in common use.

### Systemic

*Demeton-s-methyl.* This is a widely-used insecticide for most agricultural and horticultural crops, controlling aphids and red spider mites.

*Dimethoate.* This is used for the control of aphids on many agricultural crops. As an emergency treatment it can be used as a spray against wheat bulb fly.

*★Disulfoton.* This insecticide controls aphids on brassicas, beans, potatoes and sugar beet, and also carrot fly. It is used in the granular form.

*Formothion.* This controls aphids on many agricultural crops, and it can also be used in an emergency against wheat bulb fly.

*Menazon.* This insecticide controls aphids on brassicas, beans, potatoes and sugar beet. With the latter it is used as a seed dressing against an early attack.

*★Phorate.* This is used in a granular form chiefly for the control of aphids in beans, potatoes and sugar beet.

### Non-systemic

*Malathion.* This insecticide is often used in mixtures with DDT. It controls aphids in most agricultural and horticultural crops. It is also used for the control of the saw-toothed grain beetle in stored grain.

*★Parathion.* As a spray, this insecticide controls aphids on many horticultural crops. It is also used against mangold fly on the sugar beet crop.

Care in handling insecticides has already been mentioned. It is also important to remember that a certain interval must be observed between the last application of the insecticide and:

(1) harvesting edible crops,
(2) access of animals and poultry to treated areas.

With some insecticides this interval is longer than others. This is another reason for very careful reading of the manufacturer's instructions.

For up to date information on insecticides available, and the regulations and advice on the use of these chemicals, reference should be made to the annual publication of the Agricultural Chemicals Approved Scheme "Approved Products for Farmers and Growers".

NEMATOCIDES (including soil sterilants)

Nematocides are those materials developed specifically for the control of eelworm pests of crops, e.g. DD mixture or Dichloropropene used by itself.

Certain chemicals in this group are classified as *Soil Sterilants*, and these are now brought into use in field crop production, e.g. Dazomet and Methom-Sodium.

Persistency is a constant cause of concern of food producers, and research is continually directed towards finding safer less persistent compounds. As a chemical group, the *carbomates* are now being developed. To a large extent they are non-persistent, and they could have great potential—carbaryl is an example of a carbonate insecticide.

Table 20 indicates the major pests attacking farm crops and their control.

## Other Pests of Crops

BIRDS

Generally birds are more helpful than harmful, although this will depend on the district and type of farming carried out. To the grassland farmer in the west, birds are not nearly the pest they are to the arable farmer in the Midlands and East Anglia. All birds in their lifetime will eat some cereal seed, but most of them help the farmer by eating many insect pests and weed seeds, and the diet of some in addition includes mice, young rats and other rodents.

The *wood pigeon* certainly does far more harm than good. Not only does it eat cereal seed and grain of lodged crops, it also causes considerable damage to young and mature crops of peas and brassicas. The only effective ways of keeping this pest down are by properly organized pigeon shoots and nest destruction.

Table 21. Major Pests and their Control

| Crop attacked | Pest | Description | Life-cycle | Symptoms of attack | Control | Notes |
|---|---|---|---|---|---|---|
| Cereals | Adult: Click-beetle Larva: Wireworm | Adult: Brown, 6–12 mm long. Larva: Growing to 25 mm long, yellow colour. | Larvae hatch out during summer from eggs laid in the soil. They take 4–5 years to mature, and after pupation in the soil, the adult appears in early autumn. | Yellowing of foliage followed by disappearance of successive plants in a row. This is caused by wireworm moving down the row. Larvae eat into the plants just below soil surface. They are usually found in the soil around the plants. | Good growing conditions to help the crop grow away from an attack. Wheat and oats more susceptible than barley; they should not be grown where the wireworm count is over 2 million/hectare. All seed should be dressed with gamma BHC. | Do not confuse wire-worm attack with other pests such as eelworm. |
| | Adult: Cranefly Larva: Leather-jacket | Adult: Is the "Daddy Longlegs". Larva: Leaden in colour, 30 mm long. | Eggs laid on grassland or weedy stubble in the autumn from which the larvae soon emerge. They feed on the crop the following spring, pupating in the soil during the summer. | Crop dies away in patches, root and stem below ground having been eaten. Larvae found in soil. | If possible, plough the field before August to prevent the eggs being laid. DDT or BHC can be applied as a low volume spray, or a Paris green and bran bait broadcast late in the evening. Aldrin may be used on DDT-sensitive varieties of barley. | |
| | Wheat bulb fly | Larva: Whitish-grey, 12 mm long. | Eggs laid on bare soil in the autumn. Larvae feed on the crop until following May. Pupation then follows either in the soil or plant. | Central shoot of plant turns yellow and dies in early spring. Larvae found in root of plant. | If possible, avoid sowing wheat where the field has lain bare from late summer. Seed dressing using organo-mercury compound plus BHC or aldrin. The latter can only be used for autumn sown wheat up to 31st Dec. each year. In an emergency the crop can be sprayed with dimethoate and formothion. | Wheat is only attacked. |

| | | | | | | |
|---|---|---|---|---|---|---|
| Cereals | Frit fly | *Larva:* Whitish, 3 mm long. | Three generations in the year, the most important being the first when in May eggs are laid on oats. The larvæ feed on the crop, pupating in the soil in late June. | In early summer the central shoot of the plant wilts, turns yellow and dies, but the outer leaves remain green. | Sow spring oats early, and try and get them past the 4-leaf stage as quickly as possible. | Oats are attacked more than the other cereals. Spring oats are particularly susceptible. |
| | Gout fly | *Larva:* Legless, yellowish-white, 6 mm long. | Two generations in the year, the most important being the first. Larva hatch and feed in plant. | Leaf sheath surrounding the ear is swollen and twisted. Poorly developed grain emerges. | Sow the crop early. Good growing conditions will help to keep it growing well. | Barley is chiefly affected. |
| | Cereal aphids | Various species of green fly, 1·6–3·3 mm long. | Winged females found feeding on cereal crops in May and June. Wingless generations produced which continue feeding during summer. Most species move back to winter quarters (woody hosts, and some grasses and cereals, depending on aphid species) in autumn, although some may be found on young cereal crops at the end of the year, especially in the milder parts of the country. | Depending on the species, the damage caused to the cereal varies from stunted withered growth, occasionally with reddish-brown to purple spots on the leaves. The grain aphid causes empty and/or small grain; by puncturing the grain in the milk-ripe stage, the grain contents seeps out. This also reduces the weights of the grain. | The grain aphid causes most concern and experiments suggest that spraying with a systemic organo-phosphorus insecticide is advisable when more than 10 aphids are counted per shoot. | Aphids carry virus diseases from infected to clean plants. See yellow dwarf virus Table 21. |

(continued overleaf)

TABLE 21. MAJOR PESTS AND THEIR CONTROL—continued

| Crop attacked | Pest | Description | Life-cycle | Symptoms of attack | Control | Notes |
|---|---|---|---|---|---|---|
| | Stem and bulb eelworm | Too small to be seen without magnification. | Live and breed in the plant. If plant dies, eelworms become dormant in dead tissue or soil, becoming active again when conditions are suitable. | Twisting and swelling, and in many cases death of the plant. | Resistant varieties. Rotation to starve out the eelworm. Clean seed. | Attacks oats. Eelworms are not insects. |
| | Cereal cyst eelworm | Dark brown lemon-shaped cysts about 1 mm (1/25 in.) long. | Live and breed in the roots. White-looking cysts (female containing large numbers of eggs) are found on roots. Later these cysts (now dark brown) become free in the soil to infect the host plant again. | Crop shows patches of stunted yellowish-green plants. Root system very bushy. Cysts visible on roots from June onwards. | Avoid growing oats too often in the field. Grow resistant varieties, e.g. Sabarlis barley. | Oats chiefly infected, but intensive cereal growing will build up eelworm in the soil to affect other cereals. Winter wheat chiefly attacked. |
| | Slugs and snails | Field slug lightish-brown in colour, about 40mm(1½in.) long. | Wheat grain damaged by being eaten in the ground before it germinates. Young cereals can be completely grazed off by a severe autumn attack. Most active in moist and humid conditions. An attack can be more serious when the seed is direct-drilled if the slit has not been properly covered. | | Baits containing metaldehyde and methiocarb spread evenly over the field prior to drilling. Extra cultivations in preparing the seed-bed help to check the pests. | |
| Stored grain | Saw-toothed grain beetle. | *Adult:* Dark brown 3 mm long. *Larva:* White and flattened. | Eggs are laid on the stored grain; larvæ feed on the damaged grain. Pupation takes place in the grain or store. | The grain heats up rapidly; it becomes caked and mouldy. This is seen with the appearance of the beetles. | Add 2% malathion dust as the grain is fed into the store. | |

| Crop | Pest | Description | Life history | Damage | Control |
|---|---|---|---|---|---|
| | Grain weevil | *Adult:* Reddish-brown, about 3 mm long with an elongated snout. | During autumn the weevils bore into the stored grain to lay their eggs. The larvæ feed inside the grain where they also pupate. | Hollow grains. Sudden heating of the grain. Weevils found a few feet below the surface of stored grain. | See the saw-toothed grain beetle. |
| Beans | Bean aphid (black fly). | Very small oval body, black to green colour. | There are many generations in the year. In summer winged females feed on the crop; wingless generations are then produced which continue to feed. Eventually a winged generation flies to the spindle tree on which eggs are laid for over-wintering. | On all summer host plants, colonies of black aphids are seen on the stem leaves (especially the underside) and on the flowers. The plant wilts; it can become stunted and with a heavy infestation it may be killed. | Apply menazon (spray), or phorate or disulfoton granules in June. It also attacks sugar-beet and mangolds. |
| Peas, Beans and other legumes | Pea and bean weevil, and striped pea weevil. | *Adult:* Yellowish-brown with stripes of lighter 6 mm long. *Larva:* Legless, white with brown head. | During early spring eggs laid in the soil near plants. Larvæ feed on roots, whilst adults feed on leaves. Pupation takes place in the soil in mid-summer. | Seedling crops checked. U-shaped notches at the leaf margins. | Apply DDT or BHC either as a dust or spray when the attack is noticed. |

(continued overleaf

TABLE 21. MAJOR PESTS AND THEIR CONTROL—continued

| Crop attacked | Pest | Description | Life-cycle | Symptoms of attack | Control | Notes |
|---|---|---|---|---|---|---|
| Brassicae (cabbage, kale, oil seed rape, swedes, turnips) | Flea-beetle | A minute black beetle with a yellow stripe down each wing case. | Adults emerge from hibernation during late spring to feed on crops. Eggs are laid, but larvæ do little damage. Pupation takes place in the soil during the summer. | Very small round holes are eaten in the seed leaves of the plants. | Sow the crop either early or late, i.e. avoid April and May. Good growing conditions to get the crop quickly past the seed leaf stage. Seed dressing containing gamma BHC should be carried out. A dust or spray containing DDT or BHC can be applied as soon as the attack is noticed. | Sugar-beet, mangolds and cereal crops can be attacked on occasions. |
| Brassica seed crops | Pollen beetle (Blossom beetle). | Metallic-greenish black in colour, 3 mm long. | Adults emerge from hibernation during spring to feed on buds and flower parts. Eggs laid and similar damage caused when larvæ emerge. | Damaged buds wither and die, and the number of pods set is lessened. | When to spray with an organo - phophorus compound depends on the seed crop concerned and the number of adults present. Two sprays are normally needed, one at the early green bud stage and the other at the early yellow bud stage. | Extreme caution should be taken to ensure that no serious damage occurs to pollinating insects. |
| | Seed weevils. | Lead-grey in about 2·5 mm long. | From hibernation near previous year's seed crops adults lay eggs in young pods. Larvæ feed on seeds in developing pods; they leave the pods and fall to the ground where they pupate in the soil. | Seeds destroyed in pods. Holes seen in pod walls. | Spray with organo-phosphorus compound at late yellow bud stage. | As for pollen beetles. |

| | | | | | |
|---|---|---|---|---|---|
| Sugar-beet, man-golds, fodder beet | Flea beetle | See flea beetle on brassicae. | | Seed dressing is not possible. | |
| | Mangold fly | Larva: Yellow-white, legless, 20 mm long. | White oval-shaped eggs are laid in the underside of leaves in May. Larvæ bore into the leaf tissue and after about 14 days they drop into the soil where they pupate. | Blistering of leaf which can become withered. Retarded growth and in extreme cases death of the plant. | Good growing conditions to help the crop pass an attack. Spraying carried out using an organo-phosphorus insecticide when more than 25 hatched larvæ, or eggs are counted per plant in the 6–8-leaf stage. |
| | Aphids (black and green fly) | The green-fly (peach potato aphid) has a very small oval-shaped body of various shades of green to yellow. | During spring winged aphids migrate to the summer host crops. They move from one plant to another thus transmitting the virus from an unhealthy to a healthy plant. | A severe infestation can cause the death of the plant, but chiefly it will mean a bad attack of Virus yellows, as both aphids are responsible for carrying the virus causing this disease. | As for the bean aphid. |
| | Cyst eelworm | See cyst eelworm on cereals. | | Crop failing in patches. Plants which do survive are very stunted in growth. | See cyst eelworm on cereals. In some areas, by law, sugar-beet may only be grown 1 year in 4 or 5 in fields known to be badly affected. If necessary the soil can be tested for an eelworm count. |

[continued overleaf]

TABLE 21. MAJOR PESTS AND THEIR CONTROL—*continued*

| Crop attacked | Pest | Description | Life-cycle | Symptoms of attack | Control | Notes |
|---|---|---|---|---|---|---|
| | Wireworm | See wireworm on cereals. | | The roots of seedling plants are bitten off. | A seed dressing containing organo - mercury plus BHC. | |
| | Docking disorder. | A complex problem. Causes *irregularly* stunted plants with fangy root growth. Often caused by eelworms but soil structure giving poor growing conditions can be a casual factor. The disease is only found in East Anglia on sandy soils, normally alkaline with a low organic matter content. Losses can be minimized by good growing conditions. Success has been achieved by combining measures to improve soil fertility and the incorporation of pesticides such as dichlotopropene. | | | | |
| Potatoes | Peach potato aphid (greenfly) | See aphids on mangolds, sugar-beet and fodder beet. | | A bad infestation will check the growth of the plant, and potato virus diseases are spread. | Apply a granular organo-phosphorus insecticide. This will help to check the spread of virus disease by killing the aphids. A spray could also be used. | |

| | | | |
|---|---|---|---|
| | Wireworm | See wireworm on cereals. | Maincrop tubers are riddled with tunnel-like holes. | Aldrin dust or spray should be applied to the soil before planting. Lift the crop in early September if possible. |
| | Cyst eelworm | See cyst eelworm on cereals. | See cyst eelworm on cereals. | |
| | Slugs | See slugs on cereals. | Maincrop potatoes damaged by pests eating holes in the tubers. | No control method for potatoes as damage takes place after the crop has been planted. |
| | Leatherjacket | See leatherjacket on cereals. | Grass dying off in patches, the roots having been eaten away. Larvæ found in the soil. | Spray with BHC or use a bait. |
| Grass | | | | |

MAMMALS

Of the wild animals found in the countryside, those which cause most damage to crops are:

(1) *Rabbits* and *hares*—these can be very serious pests. They eat many growing crops—particularly young cereals. Organized shoots can control hares. Clearance of scrub and gassing are helpful in controlling rabbits.

(2) The *brown rat*, the worst pest of all, eats and damages growing and stored crops.

(3) *Mice*, another serious pest, damage many stored crops.

The local rodent officer will give advice on methods of extermination.

The harmless mammals, as far as crops are concerned, are:

The *badger* and *hedgehog*—these eat lots of insects, slugs, mice, etc.

The *fox*—kills rats and rabbits.

The *squirrel*—eats pigeon's eggs.

## Plant Diseases

Although there are many causes of unhealthy crops, such as poor fertility and adverse weather conditions, the chief cause is disease.

Diseases, like pests, annually cause millions of pounds worth of damage and loss to the agricultural industry.

The four main agencies of disease are:

### 1. FUNGI

Fungi are plants, but they are different from flowering plants in that they do not possess chlorophyll, i.e. the green colouring matter of leaves which is essential for photosynthesis. Therefore, as they cannot manufacture their own carbohydrate, they obtain it from living or dead plants. Thus it is convenient to divide fungi into two main classes:

(a) *Parasitic.* These are dependent on the living host. They are responsible for causing many plant diseases.

(b) *Saprophytic.* These live in dead plants. They play an essential part in helping to break down plant remains into humus.

There are many thousands of different species of fungus, the majority of which are invisible to the naked eye.

A typical fungus is composed of long, thin filaments (made up of single cells) termed *hyphæ*. Collectively these are known as *mycelium*. It is through the mycelium that the fungus absorbs nutrients from its host.

With most parasitic fungi, the mycelium is enclosed within the host (only the reproductive parts protruding), although some fungi are only attached to the surface of the host.

*Reproduction.* Fungi can reproduce simply by fragments of the hyphæ dropping off, but usually reproduction is by *spores*. Spores can be compared to the seeds in ordinary plants, but they are microscopic and occur in immense numbers. The mycelium produces pods which contain the spores, and when the pod is ripe it bursts open, thus scattering the minute spores.

*The dispersal of spores.* It is important to understand how the spores are dispersed, and so infection spread from one plant to another. And knowing the particular form of dispersal will help in deciding disease prevention and control methods.

Spores can be dispersed by:

(i) *The Seed.* The disease is carried from one generation to the next by the spores attaching themselves to the seed, e.g. covered smut of cereals.

(ii) *The Soil.* The spores drop off the host plant and remain in the soil until another susceptible host crop is grown in the field. A suitable rotation will go a long way to check diseases caused in this manner, e.g. club-root of brassicæ.

(iii) *Wind.* Spores carried through the air can spread diseases from an unhealthy to a healthy plant, e.g. cereal smut and rust diseases.

Fungi do show great specialization in that they are only parasitic to one type of host plant or a closely related plant.

The extent of the disease caused by the fungi does depend upon soil and weather conditions and also upon the state of the host crop. A healthy crop which is growing well will withstand an attack far more successfully than a stunted, slow-growing crop.

## 2. VIRUSES

The discovery of the virus is fairly recent, and because it is so difficult to isolate little is known about it. It is a very small organism indeed. Something like one million viruses could be contained on an average bacterium. Only by using electron microscopes can it be seen that plant viruses have a sort of crystalline form.

All viruses are parasitic. They are not known to exist as saprophytes. In many virus diseases the disease is not transmitted through the seed.

The virus is present in every part of the infected plant except the seed. Therefore if part of that plant, other than the seed, is propagated, then the new plant is itself infected, e.g. the potato. The tuber is attached to the stem of the infected plant, and infection is carried forward when the tuber is planted as "seed".

With most plant virus diseases, the infection is transmitted from a diseased to a healthy plant by aphids. These are sucking insects which carry the infected sap.

## 3. BACTERIA

Bacteria are very small organisms, only visible under a microscope. They are of a variety of shapes, but those that cause plant diseases are all rod-shaped. Like fungi, bacteria feed on both live and dead material. Although they are responsible for many diseases of humans and livestock, in this country they are of minor importance compared with fungi and viruses as causal agents of crop diseases.

Bacteria reproduce themselves simply by the process of splitting into two. Under favourable conditions this division can take place every 30 minutes or so. Thus bacterial disease can spread very rapidly indeed, once established.

4. LACK OF ESSENTIAL PLANT FOODS (*Mineral Deficiency*)

When essential plant foods become unavailable to particular crops deficiency diseases will appear. Most of the diseases are associated with a lack of trace elements, but shortage of any essential plant food will certainly reduce the yield, cause stunted growth, and make the crop more vulnerable to pest and disease attack (see also "Chemical Elements Required by Plants", p. 27).

## The Control of Plant Diseases

Before deciding on control measures it is important to know what is causing the disease. Having ascertained, as far as possible, the cause, the appropriate preventative or control measure can then be applied.

### 1. CROP ROTATIONS

A good crop rotation can help to avoid an accumulation of the parasite. In many cases the organism cannot exist except when living on the host. If the host plant is not present in the field, in a sense the parasite will be starved to death, but it should be remembered that:

(a) Some parasites take years to die, and they may have resting spores in the soil waiting for the susceptible crop to come along, e.g. club-root of the brassicæ family.
(b) Some parasites have alternative hosts, e.g. fungus causing take-all of wheat is a parasite on some grasses.

### 2. REMOVAL OF WEED HOST

Some parasites use weeds as alternative hosts. By controlling the weeds the parasite can be reduced, e.g. cruciferous weeds such as charlock are hosts to the fungus responsible for clubroot.

Both these preventative measures (1 and 2) illustrate the importance of having a sound knowledge of the parasites attacking crops.

3. CLEAN SEED

The seed must be free from disease. This applies particularly to wheat and barley which can carry the fungus causing loose smut deeply embedded in the grain. Seed should only be used from a disease-free crop.

With potatoes it is essential to obtain clean "seed", free from virus. In some districts where the aphid is very prevalent, potato seed may have to be bought every year.

4. RESISTANT VARIETIES

In plant breeding, although the breeding of resistant varieties is better understood, it is not by any means simple.

For some years plant breeders concentrated on what is called single or major gene resistance. However, with few exceptions, this resistance is overcome by the development of new races of the fungus to which the gene is no longer resistant.

Breeding programmes are now concentrating on multigene or "field resistance" which means that a variety has the characteristics to *tolerate* infection from a wide range of races with little lowering of yield. Emphasis is now on tolerance rather than resistance.

5. THE CONTROL OF INSECTS

Some insects are carriers of parasites causing serious plant diseases, e.g. control of the green-fly (aphid) in sugar-beet will reduce the incidence of virus yellows. Furthermore, fungi can very often enter through plant wounds made by insects.

6. REMEDYING PLANT FOOD DEFICIENCIES

In many cases a deficiency disease can easily be overcome if the deficient plant food is remedied at an early stage.

7. THE USE OF CHEMICALS

Broadly speaking, chemical control of plant diseases means the use of a fungus killer—a fungicide. A fungicide may be applied to the seed, the growing plant, or to the soil. It can be used in the form of a spray, dust or gas. To be effective, it must in no way be harmful to the crop, nor after suitable precautions have been taken, to the operator or others, and it must certainly repay its cost.

*The dressing of seed with a fungicide—seed disinfection.* This is carried out to prevent certain soil and seed-borne diseases. In many cases an insecticide is added to help prevent attacks by soil-borne pests. Various fungicides can be used, depending upon the disease to be controlled:

(a) *The organo-mercury.* They are used as a preventative measure against soil and seed-borne disease of cereals, sugar-beet, fodder beet and mangolds (available in the dry and liquid forms.)

This compound has been used for many years, but concern is now being felt about mercury levels in food, and alternatives are being sought.

Leaf spot of oats, which is more prevalent in the northern and western parts of the country, is resistant to organo-mercury, and thiram is being used instead. But with resistant strains developing, this will also hasten the development of new and safer seed dressings to replace organo-mercury.

(b) *Carboxin*—For controlling loose smut in wheat and barley.

(c) *Ethirimol*—For controlling mildew on spring barley only.

(d) *Thiram*—This is used as a dry seed dressing to prevent seed decay and pre-emergence damping-off in beans and peas and other vegetables. It also controls leaf spots in oats.

The composition of these fungicides will vary slightly according to the particular commercial brand, but they are all approximately the same, consisting of a very small percentage of the actual poison, plus a large percentage of the carrier. A dye is added so that dressed seed can easily be distinguished. The dressing of seed is preferably carried out by a seeds merchant. There should be very little extra charge.

Treated seed should be sown as soon as possible, but if temporary storage is necessary it should be kept in dry, airy conditions. It should not be used for human or animal consumption.

*Application to the plant.* A good example is the control of potato blight. The fungicide can be used as a dust or spray, and it may have to be repeated at 10–14-day intervals, according to the season.

*Copper,* and *organic sulphur* compounds, are the chemicals used for controlling blight. *Organic tin* compounds are now being used as well, and because of more persistency they give better protection for the tubers against the blight spores.

Systemic fungicides are now being developed to control potato blight.

*Tridemorph* is another specific systemic fungicide and it is used for controlling mildew on barley and oats. Further systemics are being developed for the control of cereal rusts and for rynchosporium on barley.

The near future should see broad spectrum systemic fungicides available for controlling a wide range of fungus diseases on farm crops.

*Soil use of fungicide.* Has little application in agriculture, but *dazomet* as a soil sterilant is used for controlling club root on brassicae either by dusting the seedling roots or dipping them in a paste.

Table 21 gives the main plant diseases affecting farm crops, and their control.

### Suggestions for Classwork

1. Make a collection of the most important pests attacking crops.
2. Look out for any possible pest and disease attack on crops growing in the district. Examine closely the symptoms of attack, and find out the most suitable remedy.
3. When handling insecticides and fungicides, pay every attention to the manufacturers' instructions.

TABLE 22. MAIN PLANT DISEASES AND THEIR CONTROL

| Crop attacked | Disease | Causal agent | Symptoms of attack | Life-cycle | Methods of control |
|---|---|---|---|---|---|
| Cereals | (1) Bunt, covered or stinking smut of wheat<br>(2) Covered smut of barley<br>(3) Covered and loose smut of oats | Fungus | Brown or black spore bodies instead of grain in the ears. | Infected grain is planted; seed and fungus germinate together and thus young shoots become infected. The spores are released when the skin breaks, and so combining or threshing contaminates healthy grain. | Organo-mercury seed dressing. It is unwise to dress seed with a moisture content of more than 16%. |
| | (1) Leaf stripe of barley<br>(2) Leaf stripe of oats | Fungus | The first leaves have narrow brown streaks. Subsequently brown spots appear on the upper leaves. | Infected grain is planted; seed and fungus germinate together and thus young shoots are infected. From the secondary infection, spores are carried to developing grain. | As for the covered smuts. |
| | (1) Loose smut of wheat<br>(2) Loose smut of barley | Fungus | Infected ears a mass of black spores. They do not remain enclosed within the grain as with the covered smuts. | Similar to the covered smuts, but the fungus develops within the grain. The spores are dispersed by the wind to affect healthy ears. | (1) Resistant varieties.<br>(2) Clean seed.<br>(3) Hot water treatment of suspected infected grain. A skilled operation, not done by the farmer.<br>(4) The seed can be dressed with Carboxin. |
| | Yellow rust | Fungus | Yellow coloured pustules in parallel lines on the leaves, spreading in some cases to the stems and ears. In a severe attack the foliage withers and shrivelled grain results. | The fungus mainly attacks wheat. Infection appears on the plant from May onwards. From the pustules, spores are carried by the wind to infect healthy plants. During winter, spores are dormant on autumn sown crops. | (1) Resistant varieties, although new races appear against which these varieties soon have no resistance.<br>(2) Tolerant varieties will be bred in future.<br>(3) Fungicides are becoming available for seed dressing. |

[continued overleaf

TABLE 22. PLANT DISEASES AND THEIR CONTROL—*continued*

| Crop attacked | Disease | Causal agent | Symptoms of attack | Life-cycle | Methods of control |
|---|---|---|---|---|---|
| Cereals—*continued* | Mildew | Fungus | On winter cereals, grey-white and brown mycelium on lower leaves in February. Infection spreads to other leaves and plants. Disease general between May and August. Early infected leaves go yellow and shrivelled. Towards the end of season black spore cases formed among brown fungi. | From self-sown cereals in stubble, winter and spring cereals can be infected. | (1) Clean-up old stubbles. (2) Resistant varieties, although new races of the fungus may appear to nullify previous resistance in a variety. (3) Spring barley seed can be dressed with enthirimol. (4) Barley and oats can be sprayed with a systemic fungicide—tridemorph. |
| | Leaf Blotch (Rhyncho-sporium) | Fungus | When fully-formed lentil-shaped blotches (light grey with dark brown margins) up to 19 mm (¾ in.) long are seen on the leaves. As disease progresses blotches coalesce. Not often seen before May. | Fungus over-winters on self-sown barley plants and on 2-row winter barley crops. From here spores are carried to planted barley crops. | (1) Clean stubbles of all self-sown barley plants. (2) Systemic fungicides are being developed. *Note:* Attacks only rye and barley, 6-row barley is more resistant. |
| | Black stem rust or black rust | Fungus | Reddish-brown lines or spots on the leaves and stems, later succeeded by black streaks on the foliage. | Spores are wind-borne—often over long distances —from barberry bushes and then from plant to plant. It does most damage on wheat in south-west counties. | Resistant varieties. |

| | | | | |
|---|---|---|---|---|
| Cereals—*continued* | Brown rust of barley | Fungus | Numerous, very small and scattered, orange-brown pustules on the leaves in June. These gradually develop late in the season. A severe attack causes shrivelled grain. | The resting spores overwinter on stubbles. From here the pustules are airborne to infect healthy plants. | (1) Crop hygiene to clear stubble of volunteer plants. (2) Resistant varieties. (3) A specific systemic fungicide is now available. |
| | Septoria diseases (leaf and glume blotch) | Fungus | Leaf: bleached or discoloured blotches of varying sizes and shapes (on which appear rows of minute black dots) seen from late autumn to early summer. Glume blotch: becomes prominent in July and August, especially in wet seasons. Irregular, chocolate spots or blotches on glumes, beginning at the tips; later ears become blackened with secondary infection. Leaves also show yellowish areas and fungus can affect stems and leaf sheaths as well. Shrivelled grain results. | Leaf spores are liberated in wet weather, and they winter on volunteer crops; they transfer to winter cereals and then move on to spring crops. Glume blotch has a similar life cycle, but the fungus can also be carried on the seed. | (1) Crop hygiene to clear stubble of volunteer plants. (2) Clean seed. (3) Resistant varieties. |
| | Barley yellow dwarf virus | Virus | Stunted plants in patches or scattered as single plants. Poor root development. Mostly red and yellow colour changes in leaves. Late heading and reduced yield. | The crop is infected by cereal aphids. | Spray with organo-phosphorus. (See Control of Cereal Aphids Table 21). |

[*continued overleaf*]

TABLE 22. MAIN PLANT DISEASES AND THEIR CONTROL—*continued*

| Crop attacked | Disease | Causal agent | Symptoms of attack | Life-cycle | Methods of control |
|---|---|---|---|---|---|
| Cereals— *continued* | Eyespot (sharp eyespot) is somewhat similar but not so serious | Fungus | Eye-like lesions on stem about 75 mm (3 in.) above ground. Grey "mould" inside stem; straws lodged in all directions. No darkening at base of stem. | The fungus can remain in the soil, on old stubble and some species of grasses for several years. It usually attacks susceptible crops in the young stages. | Spring sown barley and wheat are more resistant than autumn sown crops. Arrange a break of at least 2 years from cereals. Most winter wheat varieties show good resistance. |
| | Take-all or whiteheads | Fungus | Black discoloration at base of stem. Grey colour of roots. Ease with which plant can be pulled from the soil. Infected plants ripen prematurely, and produce bleached ears containing little or no grain. | Wheat and barley only affected. The fungus survives in the soil in root and stubble residues and the host plant is infected when it is grown in the field. | Rotation to starve the fungus, but after some years of continuous wheat growing, infection appears to lessen. Extra nitrogen helps the growth of new roots. Bad drainage reduces plant vigour and it is more easily damaged. |
| | Manganese deficiency of cereals | Manganese deficiency | Yellowing on leaf veins followed by development of brown lesions. With oats the spots enlarge and can extend across leaf. Thus the leaf can bend right over in the middle. Older leaves wither and die. Can lead to shrivelled grains. | | 9 kg/ha (8 lb/acre) manganese sulphate in 340 litres/ha (30 galls/acre) water., With a bad attack this may have to be repeated after 3 weeks. |
| Beans | Chocolate spot | Fungus | Small circular chocolate coloured discolorations on leaves and stems; with bad attack symptoms move to flowers and pods. In wet weather spots coalesce. | Fungus carried over from previous year on debris of old bean haulm and on self-sown plants. But infection can start from almost any dead vegetation with this widespread fungus. | Clean up stubbles containing remains of old crop of beans. Give good growing conditions. Autumn sown beans are more liable to attack than spring sown and they suffer more severely. |

| Crop | Pest/Disease | Cause | Symptoms | Description | Control |
|---|---|---|---|---|---|
| Peas | (1) Pre-emergence damping-off<br><br>(2) Foot-rots | Fungi and bacteria | (1) The seeds and young seedlings rot before the shoots emerge above ground.<br>(2) Base of stems of young plants blackened. | The organisms are soil-borne. They feed on the young plants when grown in the field, and return to the soil on the death of the plant. | Seed dressing using thiram. This has the effect of increasing the percentage emergence and stand of seedlings. |
| Brassicae (cabbage, oil seed rape, kale, swedes and turnips) | Club root or finger and toe | Fungus | Swelling and distortion of the roots. Stunted growth. Leaves pale green in colour. | A soil-borne fungus. The fungus grows in the plant roots and causes the typical swellings. Resting spores can pass into the soil especially if diseased roots are not removed. They can remain alive for several years, becoming active when the host crop is again grown in the field. | (1) *Rotation.* With a bad attack advisable not to grow the crop for at least 5 years in the field.<br>(2) *Liming and drainage.* The spores are more active in acid and wet conditions.<br>(3) *Resistant crops.* Kale is more resistant than swedes or turnips. Some varieties of swedes and turnips are more resistant than others. |
| Brassicae | Brown heart of swedes (Raan) | Boron deficiency | No external symptoms, but when the root is cut open a browning or mottling of the flesh is seen. Affected roots are unpalatable. | | See heart rot of sugar-beets. |

[continued overleaf]

TABLE 22. MAIN PLANT DISEASES AND THEIR CONTROL—*continued*

| Crop attacked | Disease | Causal agent | Symptoms of attack | Life-cycle | Methods of control |
|---|---|---|---|---|---|
| Sugar-beet, mangolds fodder-beet | Virus yellows | Virus | First seen in June/early July on single plants scattered throughout the crop—a yellowing of the tips of the plant leaves. This gradually spreads over all but the youngest leaves. Infected leaves thicken and become brittle. The yield is seriously reduced by an early attack. | The crop is infected by aphids which have overwintered in mangold clamps and steckling beds. The aphids carry the virus, and they can very quickly infect the whole crop. | (1) Good growing conditions to keep the crop growing vigorously. (2) All mangold clamps should be cleared by the end of March. If not, they should be sprayed to kill any aphids. (3) Seed crop stecklings should not be raised in the main sugar-beet areas. (4) An organo–phosphorus insecticide should be used when the aphids are first seen. This may have to be repeated at least once. A granular organo–phosphorus can be used, or the soil can be dressed with organo–phosphorus to give protection against an early attack. (5) Virus yellows tolerant varieties can be grown where the disease is a great hazard. |
| | Heart rot | Boron deficiency | In young plants the youngest leaves turn a blackish-brown colour and die off. A dry rot attacks the root and spreads from the crown downwards. The growing point is killed, being replaced by a mass of small, deformed leaves. | | This deficiency is more apparent on dry and light soils and can be made worse by heavy liming. Apply borax at 22 kg/ha as soon as the disease is seen. Use a boronated compound fertilizer on suspected soils. |

| Potatoes | Blight | Fungus | Brown areas on leaves. Whitish mould on the underside of leaves. Leaves and stems become brown and die off. | Infected tubers (either planted, ground keepers, or throw outs from clamps) produce blighted shoots. From these shoots the fungus spores are carried by the wind to infect the haulms. From the haulms the spores are washed into the soil to infect the tubers. Infection can also take place at harvest. | The disease is very dependent on the weather. Beaumont warnings can be given to growers by the Advisory Service. These indicate when conditions are most favourable to blight infection. 10–14 days' warning of outbreaks are possible, and the grower is then advised to spray or dust his crop. An early preventative application before there is any sign of attack should be given using copper, zinc, or tin compounds. Before harvesting, the haulm should be chemically destroyed to lessen the risk of tubers becoming infected as they are lifted. |
| | Leaf roll | Virus | Lower leaves are rolled upwards and inwards; they feel brittle and crackle when handled. The other leaves are lighter green and more erect than normal. Yield is lowered. | The virus is transmitted by aphids from plant to plant. Infected tubers (which show no sign of the disease) are planted and thus the disease is carried forward from year to year. | (1) Use certified "seed" which is grown in areas such as Scotland and Northern Ireland where aphids are not prevalent due to the colder climate. Thus the "seed" is free from virus infection. (2) Systemic sprays will control the aphids, and thus reduce the spread of virus, or use a granular insecticide. |

*[continued overleaf*

TABLE 22. MAIN PLANT DISEASES AND THEIR CONTROL—*continued*

| Crop attacked | Disease | Causal agent | Symptoms of attack | Life-cycle | Methods of control |
|---|---|---|---|---|---|
| Potatoes | Common scab | Actinomycete | Skin-deep irregular-shaped scabs on tuber; these can occur singly or in masses. With a severe attack cracking and pitting takes place with secondary infection by insect larvæ and millipedes. | The soil-borne organism attempts to invade the growing tuber which responds by development of corky tissue to restrict the parasite to the surface layers. Organism re-enters soil when infected seed is planted. | (1) Avoid liming just prior to planting potatoes. Disease is particularly prevalent on light sandy, alkaline soils. (2) Irrigation of dry, light soils an advantage. Dry conditions favour the spread of the disease. (3) Some varieties are more resistant than others. |
| | Mosaics | Virus | May range from a faint yellow mottling on leaves to a severe distortion of the leaves and distinct yellow mottling. Yield can be seriously reduced by the severe forms. | Some of the viruses responsible are spread by aphids but some, e.g. Virus X, are spread by contact between leaves and roots and on machinery and clothing. | As for leaf roll. |
| | Dry-rot | Fungus | Infected tubers are usually first noticed in January and February. The tuber shrinks and the skin wrinkles in concentric circles. Blue-pink or white pustules appear on the surface. | The soil-borne fungus enters the tuber from adhering soil. Infection can only enter through wounds and bruises caused by rough handling at harvest. The disease can be easily spread during storage. | (1) If the potatoes are handled carefully, infection is considerably reduced. Some varieties are more resistant than others to the disease. (2) Dust the seed with tetrachlornitrobenzene when storing. |
| | Spraing | Tobacco rattle virus (TRV) or Potato Mop-top virus (PMTV) | Foliage—very variable: TRV—stem mottling; PMTV—yellow blotches and bunching of leaves on short stems—like a mop. Tubers—primary (after soil infection): wavy or arc-like brown, corky streaks in flesh of cut tuber. Secondary—from infected tubers: PMTV—badly [...] | TRV spread by nematodes in soil, especially in light sandy soils. PMTV—spread by powdery scab fungus and can remain in the soil for years in fungal resting bodies. | Plant only resistant varieties, e.g. King Edward, Majestic, on infected soils. Do not plant tubers showing spraing symptoms or carrying much powdery scab. Seek expert advice. |

| | | | | |
|---|---|---|---|---|
| Potatoes | Blackleg | Bacteria | Plants stunted and pale green or yellow foliage; easily pulled out of the ground and stem base is black and rotted. Infected and neighbouring tubers develop a wet rot in the field or in store, especially in damp and badly ventilated (warm) conditions. | The bacteria move to tubers via the rhizomes and in wet soil to healthy tubers to enter via lenticles or damaged areas. Carried on seed tubers. | Rogue or reject seed crops where the disease shows on foliage. Do not plant infected tubers. Tuber dips may spread the disease to healthy tubers. |
| | Gangrene | Group of Phoma fungi | A serious tuber rot which develops in storage, usually late; it shows as grey "thumb-mark" depressions on the tubers and the flesh beneath is rotted; also, pin-head black spore cases. | The fungus remains alive in the soil and on trash, and can infect tubers in the soil and from tuber to tuber when handling. | Do not plant diseased seed. Assist tuber wounds to heal by keeping them warm (60°–65°F) and humid up to 14 days after any handling operation. Treat seed with butafume fumigant. |
| | Skin Spot | Fungus | Tuber symptoms develop during late storage and appear as pimple-like, dark brown, shrunken spots with raised centres. The worst damage is the destruction of the buds in the eyes of seed tubers. | Mainly spread by infected tubers. Tuber infection occurs at lifting and is worst in cold, wet seasons. | As for gangrene. |

# WORLD CROP PRODUCTION

THE demand for food supplies is continually increasing to supply the increasing world population and a higher standard of living in developing countries. Agricultural scientists are likely to play an increasingly important role in this extra production, but the situation is bedevilled by political, social, economic and religious considerations.

The earth's land surface (about 30% of total surface) can be divided approximately as follows: one-fifth is under polar ice; one-fifth desert; one-fifth mountain; one-fifth pasture and forest; one-tenth bare rock; and one-tenth is *arable land*, i.e. about 3% of the total surface area.

The most intensive agriculture in the world is in Imperial Valley, California—an area of about half a million acres.

### Land Use in the United Kingdom

*Total area:* 60 million acres consisting of approximately:
   12 million acres (20%)—mountains, forests, urban areas, motorways, etc.
   18 million acres (30%)—rough grazing, including deer forest.
   12 million acres (20%)—permanent grassland (7 years +).
    6 million acres (10%)—temporary grass (leys).
   12 million acres (20%)—arable crops.
The acreages of the various arable crops are approximately:
   9·2 million acres (77%)—cereals (3 m wheat, 5·2 m barley, 1 m others).
   0·5 million acres ( 4%)—potatoes.
   0·5 million acres ( 4%)—sugar beet.
   0·5 million acres ( 4%)—forage crops (kale, swedes, turnips, etc.).

0·2  million acres (1½%)—field beans and oil-seed rape.
0·6  million acres (4½%)—vegetables.
0·25 million acres ( 2%)—fruit.
0·25 million acres ( 2%)—other crops and fallow.
    (0·5 million acres are approximately 200,000 hectares)

# APPENDIX. METRICATION

ALL the metric units which may be used in agriculture when the change from Imperial units takes place have not been determined at the time this book goes to press—in fact, very little consideration has been given to the matter. It was therefore decided to show the changes in units which will be used and to leave out such possible units as *quintals* (100 kg); 10 quintals = 1 tonne (ton); 1 quintal (220 lb) = 2 cwt approximately (1 tonne = 1000 kilogramme).

If quintals are accepted, hundredweights (cwt) per acre can be converted to quintals per hectare approximately as follows:

$$4 \text{ cwt/acre} = 5 \text{ quintals/hectare (q/ha)}$$
$$\xrightarrow{\hspace{2cm}} \text{add } 25\% \ (\tfrac{1}{4})$$
$$\xleftarrow{\hspace{2cm}} \text{subtract } 20\% \ (\tfrac{1}{5})$$

Similarly, for pounds/bushel $\longrightarrow$ kilogramme/hectolitre
(lb/bush)  (kg/hl)
multiply by 1·25 or add $\tfrac{1}{4}$, e.g. 60 lb/bush = 75 kg/hl

Also, units/acre $\longrightarrow$ kilogramme/hectare (kg/ha)
multiply by 1·25 or add $\tfrac{1}{4}$, e.g. 40 units/acre = 50 kg/ha

Other conversions, which are close approximations, are:

| | | |
|---|---|---|
| one Imperial ton | = | one (metric) tonne (actually 1·016 tonne) |
| one hectare | = | 2·47 acres (almost 2$\tfrac{1}{2}$) |
| one acre | = | 0·40 hectare (10 acre — 4 hectare) |
| one pint | = | 0·568 litre (1 gallon = 4·544 litre) |
| one bushel | = | 36·37 litre |
| one ton/acre | | 2$\tfrac{1}{2}$ tonne/hectare (t/ha) |
| 1 lb/acre | = | 1·12 kilogramme/hectare (kg/ha) |

i.e. lb/acre → kg/ha, multiply by 1·12 (e.g. 50 lb/ac = 56 kg/ha)

1 gal/acre = 11·2 litre/hectare (l/ha)
gal/acre → l/ha, multiply by 11·2
(Note: 1·12; 11·2; 112 lb in 1 cwt)

pints/acre → litres/hectare, multiply by 1·4
1 foot = 0·3 metre
feet → metres, multiply by 0·3
yard → metre, multiply by 0·91
yards$^2$ → metre$^2$, multiply by 0·83
yards $^3$ → metre$^3$, multiply by 0·76 (Note. 1 metre$^3$ = 1 kilo litre)
e.g. 4 yards$^3$ = 3 metre$^3$ (approximately)

$$1 \text{ lb/ft}^3 \qquad = \quad 16{\cdot}0185 \text{ kg/m}^3$$

lb/ft$^3$ → kg/m$^3$, multiply by 16

Centimetres are unlikely to be used in the new metric system, except in special circumstances. In the text centimetres (cm) are used in a few places, e.g. for water capacity of soils.

# INDEX

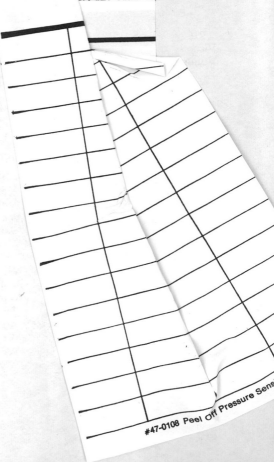